State College

at

Framingham

4-67-944877

SPACE FRONTIER

BOOKS BY DR. WERNHER VON BRAUN

FIRST MAN TO THE MOON

SPACE FRONTIER

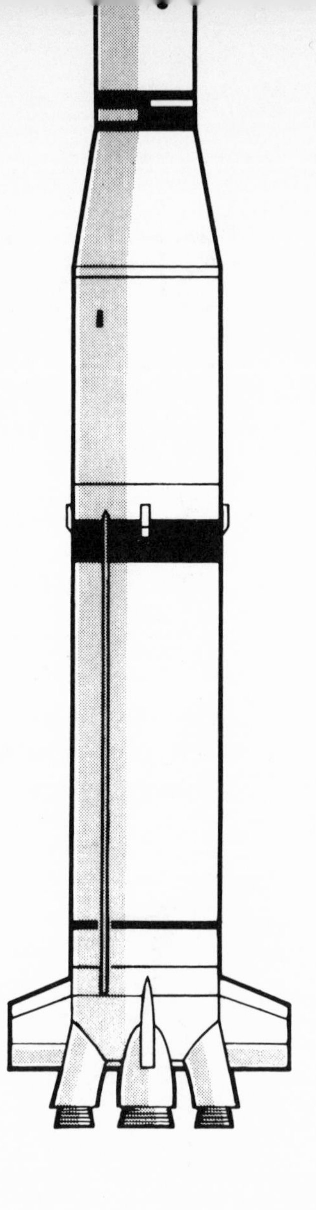

SPACE FRONTIER

BY DR. WERNHER VON BRAUN

DIRECTOR, GEORGE C. MARSHALL
SPACE FLIGHT CENTER

HOLT, RINEHART AND WINSTON
NEW YORK CHICAGO
SAN FRANCISCO

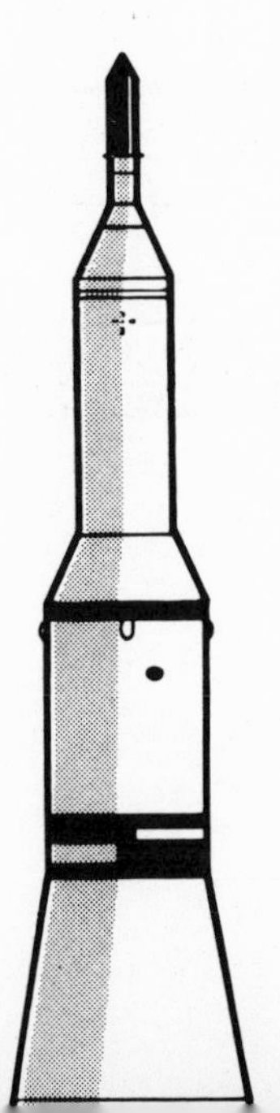

Published simultaneously in Canada by Holt, Rinehart
and Winston of Canada, Limited.

Some of the material in this volume was first published in *Popular Science* Monthly and is used with their permission.

Grateful acknowledgment is made to the National Aeronautics and Space Administration for permission to publish the photograph subsystem schema on p. 144.

Library of Congress Catalog Card Number: 67-12579 3/68

First Edition

Designer: Ernst Reichl
8637050
Printed in the United States of America

FOREWORD

This book came out of a collection of articles which I have written for *Popular Science* magazine since January, 1963. When *Popular Science* invited me to write a monthly column on my favorite subject I accepted the invitation both as a relief and a challenge. Relief, because I would have been unable to get any other work done had I attempted to answer systematically all those questions on space that found their way to my desk. Challenge, because it always intrigues me to reduce a complex problem to terms that—I hope—anyone can understand.

The problems of space flight are not like geography or astronomy or engineering or physics or chemistry or medicine. They involve a little bit of all of them and more. That's what makes it so fascinating.

But it is this kaleidoscopic aspect of space flight that made it impossible to "organize" a monthly column on the subject. Moreover, our space program is so dynamic and it moves at such a rapid pace that new facets of the kaleidoscope come into public purview with every new launching.

It is for the same reason that, when Holt, Rinehart and Winston suggested I publish this book, I did not attempt to rewrite each column and convert it into a chapter so as to come out with a well-integrated book. Instead, I limited my editorial efforts to bringing the columns up-to-date. In this process I made the gratifying discovery that it was not necessary to amend any laws of nature I had previously cited. However, I found our proper understanding of them markedly improved. If the result is a bit disjointed, it should at least be colorful.

As this book goes to print our manned spaceflight program has had its first tragedy. Gus Grissom, Ed White, and Roger Chaffe gave their lives for a cause they had often stated was worth dying for. But they met their death where they or anyone else on the Apollo program had least expected it, during a routine checkout on the launch pad. As the launch vehicle was not fueled at the time the test had not even qualified as a particularly hazardous operation.

Just before the accident, with the successful termination of the last Gemini flight, NASA had just completed the first phase of its manned spaceflight program. During this first phase 26 astronauts logged about 1900 hours in space and covered approximately 35 million miles—the distance between the earth and the planet Mars during its closest approach. This flight program was completed without loss of life or even the slightest injury to anyone, making space flight easily the most reliable transportation system ever used by man. Nevertheless, it was obvious that sooner or later statistics would catch up with our space program, too.

The death of our three Apollo astronauts makes it a duty for all of us to go on with the job with all the determination we can muster. They would not expect anything less of us.

—Wernher von Braun
Director, George C. Marshall Space Flight Center

CONTENTS

SPACE FRONTIER

I.
LAUNCH AND ASCENT

The Why and How of the Countdown

To the average TV viewer, the countdown of a big rocket is a curious space-age fad. A set of numbers flicking on the screen and a studiously unemotional voice team up in the strange ritual of counting seconds backward. Obviously invented by a showman, its sole purpose seems to be to build up tension and excitement for the audience. As the clock at last strikes zero, the show culminates in the fiery spectacle of the launch.

Probably few laymen know the real purpose of a countdown, or just how one is carried out. Actually a countdown is a carefully developed procedure of preparation for launch. Because of its tremendous importance to the success of a rocket firing, its details deserve to be better understood.

The purpose of a countdown is to:

Assure maximum safety for flight crews (if any), ground crews, and equipment, while the vehicle is prepared for flight.

Avoid wearing out critical flight or ground equipment by activating it too long before launch.

Enable the launch director to launch at an exact instant—corresponding, say, to a favorable position of celestial objects, or to requirements for orbital rendezvous.

Synchronize launch preparations with supporting operations, such as the readying of radars and tracking cameras, or the setting up of road blocks near the launch site.

For operational military rockets, the response to a firing order must be quick. Little, if any, telemetry for collecting data in flight is involved. Such a countdown may take only a few minutes.

But a complex multistage rocket carrying an equally complex spacecraft and highly sensitive research gear, whether unmanned or with a human crew, requires a countdown that may extend over many hours.

If the countdown goes according to plan, it's pretty rigid, but it offers plenty of flexibility if difficulties arise. Essential to a well-prepared countdown plan is a set, clear-cut procedure for "recycling the count."

Suppose an equipment malfunction occurs after much of the on-board guidance and radio equipment has been turned on—and an estimated two hours will be required to repair or replace the faulty part. Obviously much of the activated on-board gear should be turned off again. Therefore the countdown—already advanced, say, to T minus 7 minutes—may be cycled back to "T minus 20 and holding." This means that the count will be resumed at T minus 20 minutes whenever the repair work has been completed and the replacement part has checked out okay.

But there may be merely a temporary radio interference, clearly traced to a passing aircraft. In this case the count will be held "momentarily." No equipment will be turned off. The count will continue at the clock reading where it was stopped, as soon as the trouble clears up.

A set of emergency procedures, in a well-planned countdown, safeguards flight and ground crews and the space vehicle in the event of any serious malfunction. The proper emergency procedure must vary as the countdown clock ticks along. It undergoes drastic changes as hazardous fuel and oxidizer are pumped into a liquid rocket's tanks; again, as the servicing structure is removed from the space vehicle, and there is no longer access to certain critical stations of the vehicle. A few minutes later, after ground crews have evacuated the launch-pad area, the flight crew monopolizes the launch director's concern for safety of personnel. In case of a dangerous fire in the rocket, for example, the crew of the spacecraft may now fire its escape rocket without endangering the ground crew.

In the final phases of the countdown the text for the emergency procedures, usually printed on every back page of the countdown book, becomes longer than that for the actual launch procedures themselves.

The Cape Kennedy procedures for SA-7, our seventh Saturn I rocket launched September 18, 1964, from the John F. Kennedy Space Center in Florida, illustrate the launch preparations and the countdown of a large rocket still in the developmental stage.

It was at Cape Kennedy that the elements of this two-stage Saturn rocket had first met. The eight-engine first stage, assembled and static-tested at NASA's George C. Marshall Space Flight Center, had come to the Cape by barge. The hydrogen-oxygen powered six-engine second stage, static-tested at Sacramento, California, by its maker, the Douglas Aircraft Company, had arrived by air. From Marshall, again, had come the "instrument unit," a ring segment carrying all of the rocket's guidance and most of its radio equipment. The "boilerplate Apollo"—an unmanned, instrument-filled mockup of the Apollo spacecraft—had been flown in from the Los Angeles plant of the manufacturer, North American Aviation, Inc. Additional parts had come from NASA's Manned Spacecraft Center in Houston.

After a receiving inspection, a few days' hangar delay for "updating" (substitution of improved parts arriving belatedly by special messenger), and further checkout of "individual" and "integrated" systems, the elements of SA-7 went to the launch pad.

The first stage was erected on the platform. The second stage was piled on top of it. The small but complex instrument unit was added to the stack. Finally the Apollo spacecraft was mated to the rocket. A careful alignment check followed.

Then SA-7 was connected to the "umbilical tower." This open-grid steel structure, taller than the rocket itself, supports the "swing arms" that connect a rocket electrically, pneumatically, and hydraulically with its ground-support equipment. They disconnect and swing out of the way as the rocket begins to rise from the launch pad.

Now came many days of checking out the vehicle and its ground-support equipment together, including tests of automatic fueling procedures, on-board tracking beacons and ground tracking stations, launch vehicle-spacecraft compatibility, and radio interference. Finally an integrated "Overall Test" showed that the entire complex of flight and ground hardware was ready.

Six hours prior to the planned launch time of 10:00 A.M., the countdown began.

First came installation or activation of the vehicle's "ordnance" —which stands for anything in it that can be ignited with a pyrotechnic fuse. In SA-7 the work of the ordnance crew included the installation of:

> The ignition device of the Apollo spacecraft's escape rocket.
>
> Initiators of explosive bolts to release the spacecraft's escape tower, and to separate the second stage from the first.
>
> Initiators of explosive "cutting charges" to open the vent ports prior to ignition of the second stage.
>
> Destruct charges to destroy the vehicle in midair, in case of an erratic flight.

This job, with checks of electrical connections and circuits, took about three hours.

At T minus 3 hours the liquid-oxygen tanks were filled in the second and first stages in turn. (The kerosene tanks of the first stage had been filled days earlier.)

At T minus 2:30 the hatch to the Apollo spacecraft was closed and the service gantry was pulled back. Half an hour later the launch pad was cleared of all personnel, and liquid-hydrogen filling began. About another half-hour later, the automatic liquid-oxygen and liquid-hydrogen "topping" systems that make up for evaporation losses were activated.

At T minus 45 minutes the first-stage fuel tanks were pressurized. Various nitrogen purge lines were turned on to prevent combustible gas mixtures, caused by possible leaks, from accumulating in the craft.

At T minus 25 minutes the environmental control system in the spacecraft was activated. Five minutes later all spacecraft electronic systems were turned on—telemetry, tracking beacons, and so on.

Four minutes before launch, all electrical systems were transferred from external (ground) power to internal (on-board) power, and all electrical "bus" lines feeding into the ordnance systems were armed.

At T minus 2 minutes and 30 seconds the "firing command" was given that transferred all further duties of setting systems in operation to an automatic sequencer. From this point on the launch director and his assistants merely monitored the automatic sequence, ready to interrupt it at the slightest sign of trouble. The automatic-sequencing mechanism, however, has a rather intricate interlocking system that releases each step in the sequence only after the previous one has been correctly executed.

At T minus zero the eight engines of the first stage were ignited. One second later the umbilical swing arms disconnected and moved out of the way. The hold-down devices released at T plus 2 seconds—and SA-7 was on its way.

So there you have the why and how of the countdown. As you have seen, it is no space-age fad, but a deadly serious, carefully programed procedure, upon which depends the safety and success of a launch such as that of a great Saturn rocket.

The Automatic Checkout Gives Rockets the Green Light

Automatic checkout of a space vehicle is a method to speed up the checkout of the intricate mechanical and electrical systems that make up a multistage space rocket, the spacecraft in its nose, and the supporting launch equipment on the ground.

In the past the checkout of these systems was usually a slow and rather tedious step-by-step procedure. As space vehicles grew in complexity, more and more people became involved in this operation, and the time needed for pre-launch preparations and for the actual countdown got longer and longer.

Automatic checkout was first introduced in ground- and air-launched guided-missile systems. It is used extensively for all of our latest manned and unmanned space vehicles.

The basic idea behind automatic checkout is simple. Suppose we have a hospital with five hundred patients but only one nurse. If she were to attend all the patients by visiting five hundred private rooms, some patients might die for lack of immediate attendance. To solve this dilemma, suppose we now wire up our five hundred patients for important clinical information: fever temperature, pulse rate, breathing cycle, skin temperature, brain-wave emissions, and the like. The electrical outputs of all these gauges, which are attached to the patients' bodies, are fed into a central electronic computer.

In the magnetic memory of this computer detailed information has been stored about the permissible upper and lower limits of all the collected data. For example, a body temperature between 97.8 and 99.4 degrees F. may be considered normal for the patient in Room 278, while the actually measured 100.6 degrees may indicate that he is running a fever. The computer would alert the nurse to this irregularity and even provide her with a little print-out, which might read "R 278, T+2.0," meaning that the patient in Room 278 has a temperature two degrees higher than the average of 98.6 degrees F.

A complex space vehicle such as Saturn V/Apollo consists of virtually thousands of "patients" whose pulses and fever temperatures must be continuously monitored, to make sure that we don't launch a vehicle with a sick subsystem.

Due to the rapidity of automatic checkout, it is possible to run a complete check prior to committing the vehicle to launch, and to repeat the checkout several times during the actual countdown.

Automatic checkout of a space vehicle is not limited to the mere sampling of "status readings." The method is rendered vastly more effective by the technique of subjecting the patient to "diagnostic" electrical stimuli, strategically applied, and evaluating his response to them.

The technique may be illustrated by the example of a rocket's autopilot.

Suppose the rocket encounters some atmospheric turbulence during its flight through the air. Just like an airplane being tossed about in rough air, the rocket will yield a bit, at first, to a wind gust that is trying to throw it off course. But proper control-stick deflection by pilot or autopilot will soon compensate for the disturbance.

In a rocket's autopilot the initial deflection from the rocket's heading will manifest itself in the form of a deflection angle between the rocket's axis and the space-fixed orientation of a gyroscope. This deflection produces a corresponding electrical signal. Through the complex circuitry of a control computer, the signal will finally cause a set of hydraulic actuator pistons to deflect the swivel-mounted rocket engines. The change in direction of their thrust will restore the rocket's flight path.

To check this entire control circuit, the checkout computer simply injects into the control computer an electrical stimulus signal that imitates an electrical deflection signal from the gyroscope. This makes the control computer *think* there is a deflection angle at the gyro.

Responding to the stimulus signal, the rocket-borne control computer processes the instruction, and causes the actuators to deflect the rocket engines.

The checkout computer compares the stimulus and response—the electrical stimulus signal, and the electrically indicated engine deflection that results. It consults its own magnetic memory for permissible deviations from the normal response. In this way it decides whether the circuits involved are "normal" or "sick."

Modern automatic checkout systems can handle vast quantities of such checking operations in a short time. Since digital techniques are used throughout, all signals flowing back and forth between the ground-based checkout installation and the space vehicle consist of rapid-fire bursts of simple electrical impulses.

This makes it relatively easy to run an automatic checkout, over a radio link, even after launch and while a rocket is in flight.

In the Saturn/Apollo lunar-landing program it is definitely planned to check out the third stage and the instrument and guidance compartment of the Saturn V once more after it has been injected into its parking orbit. We want to make sure in this way that everything is still shipshape, before the astronauts restart this stage and continue their voyage to the moon.

One particular automatic safety feature deserves special mention in connection with automatic checkout. Large, multi-engine rockets must be prevented from taking off with inadequate thrust. To accomplish this, the rocket is fixed to the launch platform by a multiple clamp-down mechanism, which is released only after there is clear evidence of adequate rocket-engine performance.

The technique of holding rockets down during thrust build-up was tried, off and on, during the early years of guided-missile development. It became standard procedure with the advent of multiengine rockets because of the obvious hazards involved in a takeoff with one faulty or inoperative rocket engine.

In launching large multiengine rockets, such as Atlas or Saturn, at least one characteristic indication of adequate engine performance (such as combustion-chamber pressure) is piped into the control room for all engines involved in the takeoff. The decision to release the clamp-down mechanism (commonly called the "tail grab") is made by the launch director on evidence that all engines are "in the green." In modern lanuch facilities the procedure is often automated; that is, the tail-grab signal is activated automatically when all engine read-outs are within pre-specified limits. All engines are shut off if this condition is not met within a few seconds.

How Rockets Are Steered and Guided

Methods for steering large rockets during powered flight all have one principle in common: The rocket exhaust is deflected in a controlled fashion.

For a rocket to fly straight, the force of its thrust must be so aligned as to point to the rocket's center of gravity. If the thrust force F is out of alignment and passes the center of gravity at a distance L, a turning moment will result that is equal to $F \times L$. A large rocket is steered by shifting this turning moment to the right and left (controlling yaw), or up and down (controlling pitch), depending on which way we want it to turn.

The force of a rocket's thrust is always parallel to that of the flow of exhaust gas, but acts in the opposite direction. In a liquid-propellant rocket, the combustion chamber with the exhaust nozzle is usually swiveled to and fro like the outboard motor of a small boat. The swiveling forces are provided by hydraulic actuators (oil-driven pistons) which are controlled by electrical signals from the rocket's control computer.

Older types of liquid-fuel rockets were often controlled by jet vanes. Usually there were four relatively small rudders of graphite, tungsten, or an ablative material—one whose expendable outer surface is allowed to char or volatilize—that were immersed in the main jet and rotated by electric actuators. Jet vanes do not deflect the entire jet but only part of it. The effect of a jet vane can be compared with that of a rudder located in the propeller down wash of a larger inboard motorboat.

Unlike liquid-fuel rockets, solid rockets do not have separate thrust chambers. In a solid rocket the basic airframe serves simultaneously as propellant-storage container and thrust chamber, and swiveling the thrust chamber would not be feasible. For this reason designers of solid rockets have developed deflectable exhaust nozzles. Often a single solid rocket discharges its exhaust gas through four parallel-mounted swivel nozzles, permitting complete three-dimensional control in the up-and-down (pitch), the right-and-left (yaw), and the rotational (roll) directions.

Whatever methods we use to generate adequate steering forces, the control actuators must be directed by proper signals to keep it on its prescribed flight path despite disturbances by wind, or by slight deviations from the rocket's standard weight or performance. A guidance system must be provided which continuously generates commands that correct the rocket's motion. We can take our choice of two fundamentally different guidance systems: remote control or inertial guidance.

Guidance commands may be generated by tracking the rocket with optical instruments, radar, or radio, and comparing the *actual* track with the *prescribed* flight path. A remote-control command passed on by radio instructs the speeding rocket to reduce any difference between "is" and "should be" to zero.

Such guidance systems, based on remote control by radio, have several basic drawbacks. For one, they are subject to intentional as well as unintended interference, which makes them particularly vulnerable in military operations. For space-flight operations, an even more serious drawback lies in the fact that it is impossible to maintain radio contact between ground station and rocket except along a line of sight between them. For economy in consumption of propellant, an orbital rocket must ascend to its orbit along a very shallow trajectory—and so the burn-out point of the last rocket stage is frequently well below the horizon of the launching site.

In deep-space missions the rocket may stay in one or several "parking orbits," and must restart its engine at a very precise instant for the ensuing power maneuver that leads to injection into a trajectory to the moon or the target planet. The obital restart point may be over Australia or the Pacific Ocean, while the launching was from Cape Kennedy, Florida. Radio-guidance schemes for such operations would involve a complicated globe-circling network.

An *inertial* guidance system does away with all these communication difficulties by generating the guidance commands *on board the rocket*. Such a system is entirely self-contained.

The basic idea behind an inertial-guidance system for a rocket is to measure its accelerations in three "orthogonal" (mutually perpendicular) directions, such as up-and-down, right-and-left, fore-and-aft. The three accelerations then are "integrated," an operation that a following paragraph will make clear, to obtain the velocity in each direction. In turn, the three velocities are integrated to get the *displacement,* or distance traveled, in each direction. This answers the rocket's ever-repeated query, "Where am I?"

Knowing from an electronic memory where the rocket *ought* to be at any moment, and noting any deviation, the guidance system produces the needed commands to correct the flight path.

The heart of any inertial-guidance system is thus a set of three orthogonal accelerometers to measure the three components of the rocket's acceleration.

Acceleration is what sports-car drivers call "getaway." It manifests itself as a force that presses the driver against his seat back when he steps on the accelerator. This force is the result of his body's inertia, which resists the sudden change of pace—whether the car is accelerating from a standstill or from 40 to 60 m.p.h. to pass a lumbering truck.

There are many types of accelerometers, but they all measure that "force against the seat back" due to the inherent inertia of mass. The simplest is the spring-mass accelerometer in my sketch.

As the rocket accelerates in the direction shown by the arrow, the inertia of the mass causes it to lag behind, stretching spring A and compressing spring B. A sliding-contact variable resistor, labeled "pickoff potentiometer," produces a voltage that corresponds to the acceleration at any instant.

The speedometer in our sports car clearly indicates that the

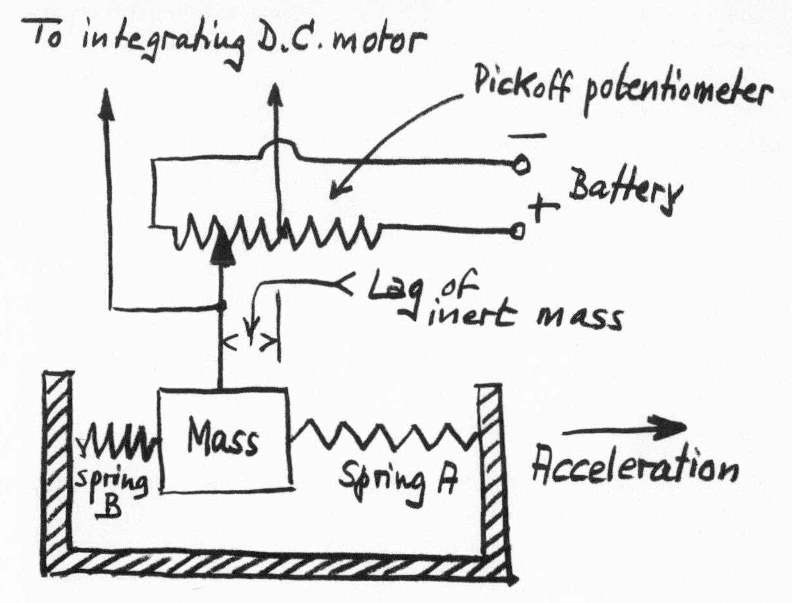

velocity is increasing, second by second, as long as we feel that pressure against the seat back. Of course, the speedometer is rigged to the wheels and really tells how fast they're spinning. But we could build another speedometer around our spring-mass accelerometer:

Suppose we drive a little DC electric motor with the voltage from the accelerometer's pickoff potentiometer. The motor will spin as long as there is an acceleration; stop as soon as it ends.

The speed at which the motor's armature revolves corresponds to the voltage supplied by the pickoff potentiometer, which in turn corresponds to the acceleration. But the total number of turns that the armature makes, over a given period of time, corresponds to the velocity built up as a result of the acceleration during that same period.

Thus, all we have to do to get our accelerometer-driven speedometer is to attach an indicator needle to the armature of the little motor—over a high-gear ratio, of course. Our new speedometer is the prototype of what guidance people call an "integrating accelerometer."

We could stick a second potentiometer on the needle axis of our new instrument and drive a second electric motor with the voltage output. Since the picked-off voltage corresponds to the car's velocity, the second electric motor will spin at a rate corresponding to that velocity; and the total number of revolutions made by its armature will correspond to the distance traveled by the car. A needle attached to the second motor, again over a high-gear ratio, will show the mileage covered—giving the same reading as the car's standard odometer. (The latter counts the total number of turns made by the wheels.) With the second electric motor we've performed the "second integration"—we have integrated velocity over time elapsed and found the distance traveled.

There is a good deal more to designing a practical rocket guidance system. In particular the designer is confronted with two principal kinds of difficulties:

1. The rocket changes its attitude throughout the flight. At takeoff it stands upright. At injection into orbit it speeds along horizontally. Moreover, as it passes through the atmosphere, it is tossed around by turbulence and shifting wind, changing its attitude temporarily.

   Our three orthogonal accelerometers must therefore be placed on a gyroscopically stabilized platform. However the rocket may turn and waver, the three accelerometers will now have and retain a fixed orientation in space. To meet the stringent accuracy requirements of inertial-guidance systems for space rockets, the stabilized platform must maintain its angular position within a fraction of a degree for several hours.

2. Any mass permitted to make constrained movements is subject to friction. In our spring-mass accelerometer, for instance, the inert mass is constrained by springs, whose stretching or squeezing involves some friction. (Just bend a piece of wire a few times rapidly, and feel the heat produced by the friction!) Also, unless the accelerometer operates in a vacuum, there will be air friction. The potentiometer pickoff is another source of friction.

All this friction reduces the accuracy of the whole system. It is no overstatement to say that the success of modern inertial-guidance systems is the direct result of a relentless fight against friction. Many methods have been tested in this fight:

There are "flotation bearings" where the suspended mass floats in a fluid of equal density. There are "gas bearings" in which the suspended mass rides upon a cushion of air or nitrogen. There are electrostatic supports, and even magnetic supports, which utilize the strange effects of electrical superconductivity at extremely low temperatures.

Accuracy of the system is improved, too, by increasing the forces created by acceleration. Gyro accelerometers, utilizing the phenomenon of gyroscopic "precession," have proved superior to simple mass-spring accelerometers.

Further gains in accuracy have come from performing integration operations, not with friction-plagued electric motors but with friction-free electronic digital computers.

Present-day inertial-guidance systems can place a satellite in orbit with an injection accuracy of a few feet per second in velocity and a fraction of a mile in altitude.

Tiny Computers Steer the Mightiest Rockets

Dramatic progress in the miniaturization of electronic equipment is, without doubt, one of the most important reasons for the rapid advances in rocket and space-flight technology in recent years.

Of course, manned orbital flights would not have become possible without the great strides made in rocket propulsion, new materials, new structural-design methods, advanced hydraulic systems, high-precision gyroscopes, and in other fields. But without the recent contributions of solid-state physics and the resulting technology of microelectronics, most of our achievements in space, whether with manned or unmanned vehicles, could not have come about.

The accompanying pictures tell, better than words, how far the art of miniaturizing electronic components has come. From the vacuum tube, progress has led to the kind of transistor in a transistor radio—and thence, in turn, to the near-microscopic chip transistor or "unit logic device." Many thousands of these ULD chip transistors are used in the microelectronic circuits of the guidance computer that IBM is developing for the Saturn V moon rocket.

Shown in the pictures is a typical ULD module about 3/10 of an inch square, in which IBM incorporates the chip transistors. They are the squares attached at junctions to the circuit pattern on

(*Left to right*) vacuum tube, transistor, and chip transistor or "unit logic device" (speck within circle) used in computer for rocket.

the top surface of the module. Dark areas, seen on the bottom surface only, are resistors formed by a screen-printing process and then trimmed to the desired resistance. Thirty-five of the modules make up a plugable "page," and the guidance equipment employs 150 such pages. The savings in weight and size of an electronic computer based on these design principles are amazing. The Saturn V guidance computer, together with its companion data adapter (which serves as a link between the computer and all other elements of the guidance system), has 80,000 components. It can perform 9,600 operations a second. Its magnetic-core memory has a storage capacity of 460,000 bits (memory elements). Yet the two boxes weigh only 267 pounds and they occupy a combined volume of only 5½ cubic feet. Almost equally astounding, the two units use a total of only 438 watts, about a quarter as much power as a household electric iron.

But the savings in weight, volume, and power requirement are possibly exceeded in importance by the tremendous inherent reliability of solid-state computers. The Saturn V computer is being built against a specification for a reliability of no less than 25,000 hours' "mean time between failures," and there is every reason to believe that this will be excelled.

A trick greatly contributing to this phenomenal reliability is the generous use of "triple modular redundancy," in connection with so-called "majority-rule voter circuits":

In laying out the design for this computer, IBM identified seven vital functional sections that could cause catastrophic failure of the space vehicle—and where, therefore, computer failures could not be allowed to occur. Then they arranged the computer in such a

On top of pencil eraser—7 chip transistors.

Thirty-five IBM modules with "ULD" chips make up a pluggable "page," and a hundred and fifty such pages go into a rocket's guidance equipment.

way that all computational problems arising in these seven critical functional sections are handled simultaneously by sets of three exactly similar but independent logic modules, arranged in parallel.

The independently derived results are channeled to majority-rule voter circuits that accept "A" as the correct answer as long as two out of the three modules present "A" as their answer. In other words, if one of the three parallel modules comes up with a different answer, it is outvoted by a majority of two to one. The probability of two modules making the same mistake is, of course, utterly remote.

The combination of speed, memory capacity, and reliability of the Saturn V guidance computer and its companion data adapter

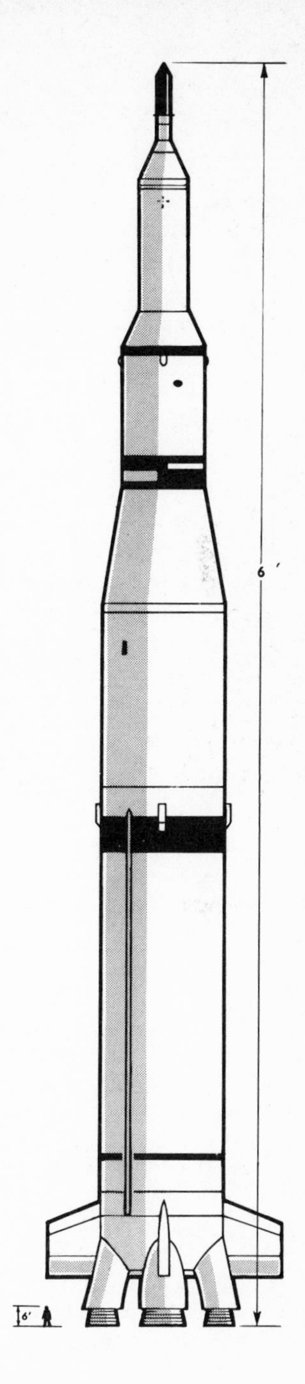

The gigantic Saturn V moon rocket as compared with the size of a man.

enables the two units to perform a number of functions that, just a few years ago, would have sounded fantastic. For instance, they provide so-called "path-adaptive guidance."

Path-adaptive guidance means that as the big rocket climbs into orbit, the computer continously compares the flight path with the optimum trajectory along which orbital injection may be attained with a minimum expenditure of propellants. It automatically corrects the flight path to follow this optimum trajectory. For example, should one of the five rocket engines of the second stage suddenly quit, the guidance computer would quickly take account of the loss in acceleration—and determine the optimum path to be flown under the power of the remaining four engines.

In addition, the two units help to perform pre-launch checkout, as well as checkout in parking orbit. During the pre-launch period, the computer can perform a self-test and a complete launch-vehicle mission simulation. In parking orbit it is used not only to recheck the guidance-and-control system but also the propulsion system of the Saturn V's third stage. In this manner it helps to make certain that the entire space vehicle, after ascending to orbit, is still in perfect condition—so that the Apollo astronauts can safely commit themselves to continue their voyage to the moon.

Will Astronauts "Fly" Rocket Boosters?

There is really no obvious reason why rocket boosters cannot be flown by manual control. Of course the stringent accuracy requirements of orbital and other space missions make it mandatory that the rocket follow a precisely planned trajectory. Manual flight, therefore, does not do away with the need for an accurate guidance system. It merely puts the pilot into the loop of executing the guidance signals. This, however, may offer distinct advantages, as we shall see.

Currently, all large rockets are led along their paths by radio guidance or by inertial guidance. In either case, two signal's are produced aboard the rocket. One says "up" or "down"; the other "left" or "right." In all space rockets flown so far, whether manned or unmanned, these two guidance siganls have been wired directly into the autopilot. Through deflection of jet vanes, rocket nozzles, or entire rocket engines, the autopilot has then actually controlled the rocket's flight.

To "fly" a rocket booster manually, an astronaut could very well take over the function of the autopilot. The guidance signals, instead of being wired directly into the control "loop," would have to be displayed on the instrument panel in suitable form for the astronaut to see and act upon.

This display could take the form of the conventional ILS (instrument landing system) indicator used by aircraft in instrument approaches to runways during conditions of low ceiling and poor horizontal visibility.

The ILS indicator has two crossing needles. One, the "localizer needle," turns right and left. The other, the "glide-slope needle," moves up and down. (See my sketch.)

In order to stay lined up with the runway, the pilot has to keep the vertical (localizer) needle centered. To descend so that he touches down at the near end of the runway, without hitting a tall building on the approach path or overshooting the runway, he has to center the horizontal (glide-slope) needle.

The basic problem of keeping a manually flown rocket on the prescribed boost trajectory is just the same as the instrument-landing problem. The only difference is that the term "climb slope" replaces "glide slope."

The possible advantages of flying rocket boosters manually can probably best be determined by looking again at time-tested procedures in aviation.

There is no technical reason in the world why the signal outputs of an aircraft's localizer and glide-slope receivers could not be fed directly into the plane's autopilot. In many aircraft it can even be done just by flipping a switch.

The sober fact of the matter, however, is that no airline in the world has yet authorized low-ceiling instrument approaches to be flown all the way to touchdown with the autopilot engaged. The reason is very simple. By removing himself from the "loop," the pilot loses that intimate touch with the situation that is required for corrective action in case of a sudden instrument failure.

Such a failure is not critical when the aircraft is several thousand feet up, where there is plenty of time for remedial action. But

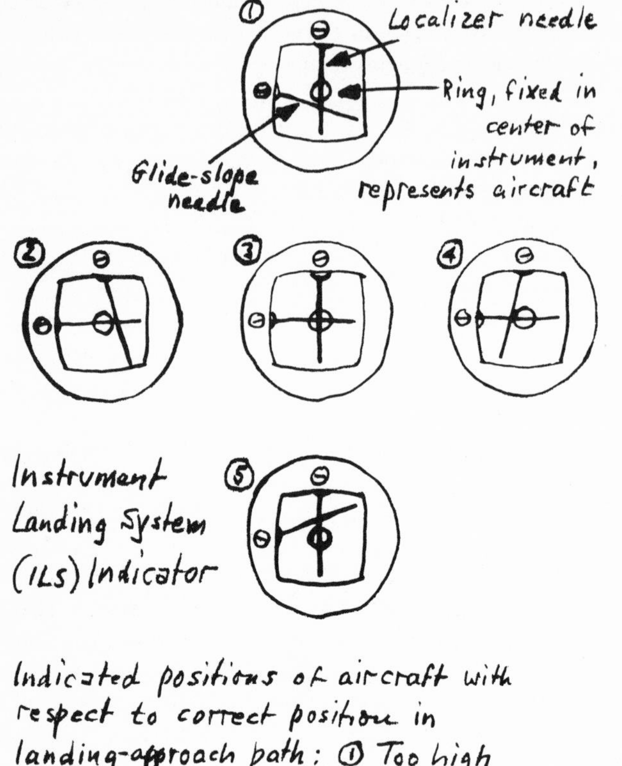

if a faulty autopilot produces, say, a hard-over, nose-down elevator deflection while an aircraft is coming in for a landing at 130 knots and just breaking out of a 200-foot overcast—well, there just isn't much time for the captain to make the transition from automatic to manual mode.

The same case can be made, and has been made, for manual control of rocket boosters during ascent. Suppose, during the high-speed ascent through the denser layers of the atmosphere, that a faulty servo actuator produces a hard-over deflection of one of the booster's rocket engines. How many seconds are left before aerodynamic forces will rip the booster apart and turn it into a fireball?

When must the astronaut in command make the fateful decision to abort the flight by separating his spacecraft from the failing booster and firing his escape rocket?

Not being "in the loop," he, too, may lose critical seconds in transition. This in turn may lead to the requirement of providing for "automatic abort"—and, needless to say, any such thing is exceedingly unpopular with astronauts. And rightfully so; for it is like telling a jet pilot, "Your plane is wired so that your ejection seat may be fired at any moment that a little black box decides you are in trouble."

However, manual control of boosters may also have certain disadvantages. One of the arguments against manual control is that a multistage space rocket would change its response to control-stick action continuously.

First, the aerodynamic forces change from zero (on the pad), through a maximum (usually a little over a minute after takeoff), and back to zero (in airless space). Second, since most of the takeoff weight is made up of propellants, the rocket loses a lot of mass as it builds up speed. Third, the occasional shedding of a stage, and the firing-up of the next-higher stage, further affect the control-stick response. Of course, all these variations can easily be compensated for electronically. But then the question arises as to what will really have been gained by putting the astronaut into the control loop, if we still depend on so much automatic equipment.

An argument in favor of manual controls is that simulator tests have conclusively shown that the structual loads encountered by a rocket while penetrating zones of high turbulence or abrupt changes in wind velocities can be substantially reduced by manual flight. This is in accordance with the well-established fact that an aircraft manually flown through severe turbulence offers a smoother ride and is subjected to less structural load than if it is "barreled through" on autopilot.

However, with our very limited practical experience in manned space flight, it would probably be premature to try to settle the issue of automatic vs manual controls of manned space rockets at this point in time.

It is likely that the question of manual booster control will come up again and again in the future. As the traffic density of our spaceflight operations increases, the question of recoverable and reusable boosters is bound to attract more and more attention. And, obviously, by the time we put a pilot in a booster to fly it back, we must be prepared to say clearly whether or not he should also fly it up.

Why Rockets Have Fins

The fins on rockets serve the same purpose as an arrow's tail feathers. They provide aerodynamic stability during flight through the atmosphere by pulling the so-called Center of Pressure (C.P.) behind the Center of Gravity (C.G.).

Let us experiment with an arrow. We remove the head and tail feathers and shoot the bare stick from a bow. It tumbles wildly. We replace the head and shoot again. The tumbling is slowed. We stick the tail feathers back on, and the arrow flies straight. Now, let us look into this varying behavior.

The bare stick's Center of Gravity is at its geometrical center (as balancing it on a wedge verifies). So long as the stick flies straight (Case 1 in my sketch), the combined retarding force due to air drag will pass through the Center of Gravity. Since there is no leverage between the force and the C.G., there can be no stabilizing or destabilizing moment (turning effect).

But now assume that for some reason—say a crosswind or gust —an ever-so-slight misalignment occurs between the aerodynamic force and the stick's center line (Case 2 in sketch). The air stream now hits the stick at an "angle of attack," α (alpha). In the sketch the fictitious force pushing against the stick at one point represents the combined effect of all the tiny little forces on the stick's entire surface. The Center of Pressure, by definition, is the point where this fictitious force intersects the stick's center line—and in Case 2, it is forward of the C.G. Acting on a lever arm l, it creates a moment that tends to *increase* the angle of attack. This condition is called *aerodynamic instability*.

Why is the Center of Pressure *forward* of the geometrical center? Air pressure is highest at the blunt frontal area—where onrushing air is brought almost to a stop before being swept aside. (This is obvious in the case of zero angle of attack, and still holds true for a moderate angle of attack.) *Ram drag* created by this frontal area considerably exceeds the air's *friction drag* along the side of the stick. So most of the drag occurs in the forward part of the stick.

When we reattach the arrowhead (Case 3 in sketch), the heavy load moves the Center of Gravity forward—but still not as far forward as the Center of Pressure. Two factors cause the slower tumbling: We have shortened the lever arm between C.P. and C.G., reducing the destabilizing moment; and by adding weight to the arrow's nose, we have increased the inertia of its mass and, thus, its resistance to abrupt rotational movements.

The arrow flies straight when we stick the tail feathers back on (Case 4 in sketch) because, as soon as an angle of attack develops, the winglike feathers generate aerodynamic lift forces—which, acting on a lever arm *l*, tend to *decrease* the angle of attack. This condition is called *aerodynamic stability*.

On rockets, fins are used because in many cases it is desirable to give a rocket aerodynamic stability.

Some rockets have fins while others don't. It depends upon how

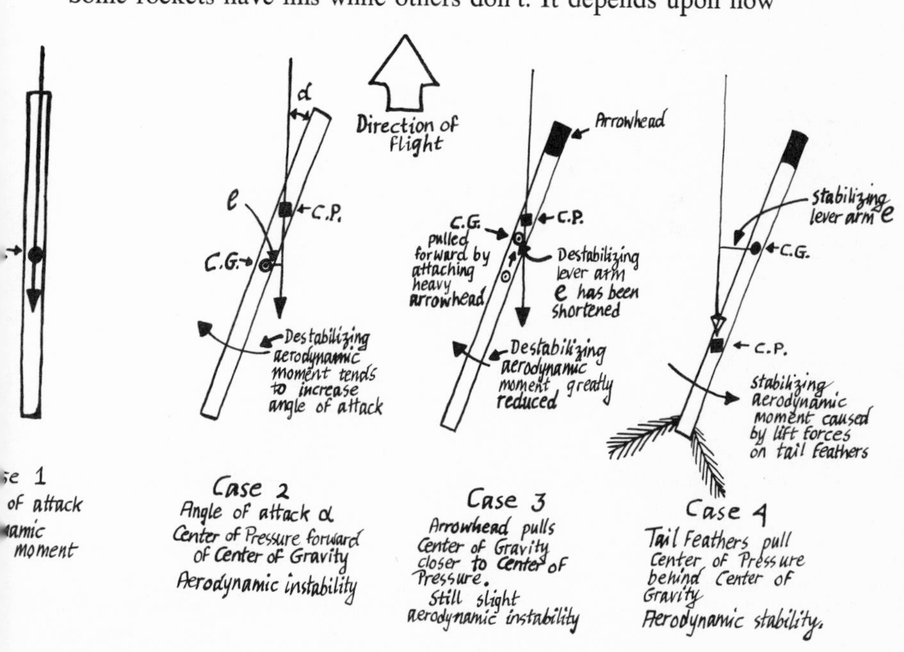

important it is, in any particular case, to improve a rocket's aerodynamic stability.

Today, autopilot sytems are available with fast enough response to steer rockets through the atmosphere no matter how unstable they are aerodynamically. Fins cost weight and drag, and can easily get misaligned by rough handling.

Therefore, all our modern long-range military missiles are finless—Minutemen and Polaris, and their predecessors Atlas, Titan, Jupiter, and Thor.

To steer aerodynamically unstable rocket missiles through the atmosphere is no mean trick. In the early days of missilery it just couldn't be done. That's why the V-2, Corporal, Viking, Sergeant, and Redstone sported fins.

The problem was not only the lack of adequate autopilots to cope with aerodynamic instability. Even more critical was the difficulty of pinning down the exact operating criteria to which the autopilot had to be tuned.

A typical long-range rocket takes off at velocity zero and a launch-site elevation not too far from sea level.

In a minute or so it reaches Mach 1, the velocity of sound; and a minute later it is speeding along through airless space at between Mach 5 and 15. During all this time the rocket's Center of Pressure travels quite a bit up and down, being highly sensitive to the Mach number at any instant. Meanwhile the Center of Gravity moves back and forth as the rocket burns up its propellants. (See my sketch.)

Simultaneously the rocket's mass is rapidly shrinking—and with it, the all-important "mass moment of inertia," the ability of the rocket's mass to oppose abrupt rotational movements.

Thus it is quite a trick to devise a rocket autopilot that can adequately cope with all these rapidly varying conditions. In fact, it is possible only by changing the "gain settings," the autopilot's tuning, several times in flight. Understandably, this rather sophisticated technique was not available for the early "birds." But today it is old hat.

Some rockets are still built with fins, for they offer great advantages in two particular applications:

One is for *antiaircraft (and antimissile) rockets.* Unlike a long-range rocket, whose usual purpose in life is to carry a warhead

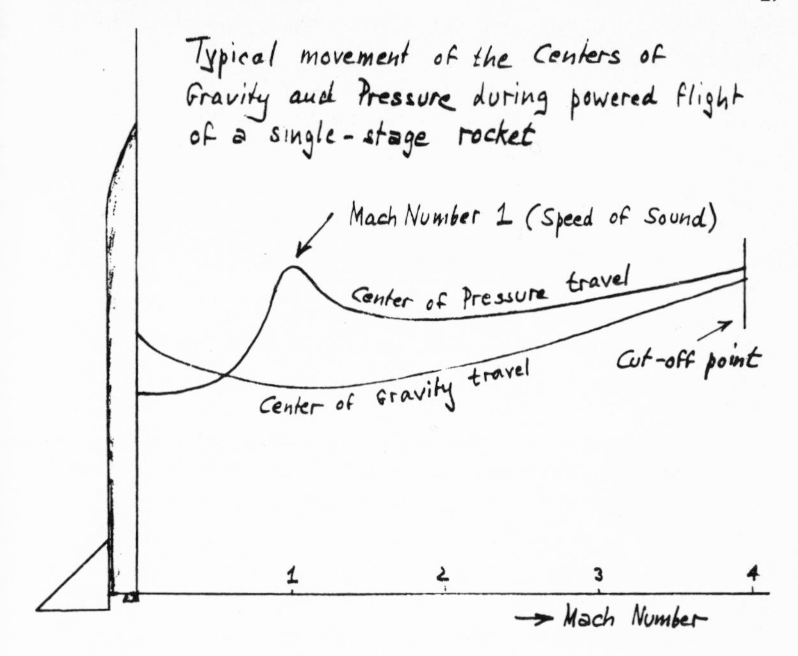

from point A to a well-defined and stationary point B, the antiaircraft or antimissile rocket doesn't know, at the instant of takeoff, exactly where its warhead will go off.

Since the target may perform evasive maneuvers, the intercepting rocket must continuously adapt its own flight path accordingly, on the basis of latest radar information of the target's movement. It has been suggested to use "path adaptive adjustments" of the autopilot, but antiaircraft-missile designers still prefer fins to simplify their complex control problem.

Antiaircraft rockets usually have rather large fins on their booster stages. During the boost phase, these rockets often fly without any active guidance or control—depending solely on their arrow stability and aimed only in the general direction of intercept, with the aid of ground launchers that can be rotated in azimuth and elevation. Only after booster drop-off does the rocket's guidance system take over.

For *manned rockets,* too, fins offer a definite advantage. Since the flight path—usually into orbit—is predetermined, and thus ideally suited to programed changes in gain setting, it might appear that there should be no need for fins. The problem of manned rockets, however, lies in the area of emergency provisions—more specifically, in what we call "abort procedures."

Suppose a large launch vehicle such as Saturn V has a serious autopilot failure at the most critical part of its ascent through the atmosphere—the "high-stagnation-pressure" period when the speeding rocket bucks the most severe aerodynamic forces. A failure in a swivel actuator may throw one of the five booster engines into a "hard-over" deflection, while an additional electrical failure may prevent the other engines from counteracting the unwanted turning moment.

In such a case, if high inherent aerodynamic instability assisted in rapidly increasing the angle of attack, structural overload might break up the rocket before the astronauts in the Apollo Command Module, triggering their escape rocket, could put a safe distance between themselves and the ensuing fireball in the sky.

It is in this area of crew safety that fins come in handy. In Saturn V the booster fins are not used to provide perfect aerodynamic stability under all conditions—that would take fins of excessive size. But the fins reduce the aerodynamic instability enough to make sure that the astronauts can safely abort, no matter what technical trouble may afflict their space vehicle.

Our aim is to reduce the "turning rate"—the rotational speed at which the aerodynamically unstable Saturn V, when stricken by an autopilot failure, would turn into an angle of attack at which its structure would be bound to fail. One might say the purpose of the fins is to extend the period of grace that the astronauts have to get away from an impending explosion caused by structural failure.

Solid vs. Liquid Rockets

A comparison of the merits of a liquid-propellant or solid-propellant rocket depends entirely on the application. Just as a gasoline engine has advantages and disadvantages compared to a diesel engine, the liquid-rocket engine is superior to the solid-rocket engine in some applications, and inferior in others. And just as the two types of piston engines are still around, after half a century of heated debate about their pros and cons, it is most likely that fifty years from now there will still be both liquid- and solid-propellant rocket engines in practical use.

The advantages of the liquid-propellant rocket—of which the Atlas and Saturn are examples—lie in its higher performance, its simple shutdown and restart capability, and the fact that it lends itself readily to a number of important control features. For example, the thrust of a liquid-propellant rocket can be varied at will, by throttling the propellant flow, and the rocket can easily be steered in flight by swiveling the relatively small engine or engines.

The advantages of the solid-propellant rocket—the Minuteman and Polaris are of this kind—lie in its inherent simplicity. It need not be fueled just prior to launching. It needs no pressure system or pumps to feed the propellants from the tanks into the combustion chamber, since the rocket's case combines the functions of both. The resulting simplification and speedup of launch preparations makes the solid-propellant rocket especially attractive for military applications where quick response may be vital.

The Chinese, who are credited with the first demonstration of rockets in the thirteenth century, probably used black powder. That age-old concoction of charcoal, sulfur, and saltpeter was faithfully used in all war, signal, and ship-rescue rockets until the end of World War I. Only in 1918 did the American, Robert H. Goddard, first try to burn *smokeless powder* in rockets. And only

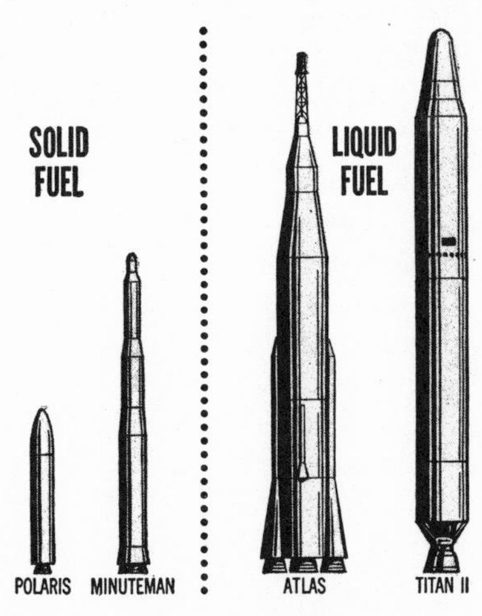

after World War II did the chemical industry come forth with high-energy composite propellants that enabled solid rockets to invade the field of long-range ballistic missiles, hitherto held uncontestedly by the more-powerful liquid rockets—and to force the liquid rockets right out into the even-more-demanding field of outer space.

Composite propellants consist mainly of a more-or-less rubbery fuel binder, in which saltlike crystals of oxidizing agents are embedded. A typical mixture may contain as much as eighty percent by weight of these crystals and still retain an amazing degree of plasticity.

There are several types of fuel binders, which differ in performance, price, high and low temperature qualities, storability, and so forth. The one quality they all have in common is long names. There are vinylpolyester, polyurethane, and polyvinyl chloride binders, just to name a few. The oxidizing agents, not to be outdone, bear labels such as ammonium perchlorate, ammonium nitrate, or potassium perchlorate. To increase combustion temperature and fuel performance, aluminum powder is sometimes added to the mixture. Finally, composite propellants usually contain a small percentage of additives to serve as combustion catalysts, chemical stabilizers, or flash suppressors, or to provide certain physical properties otherwise lacking.

Probably the most important rule in designing solid-propellant rockets is Piobert's Law, which states that the flame front always eats its way into the solid propellant in a direction normal (perpendicular) to its surface. Thus, if we fill a tube completely with rocket propellant and light it at one end, the propellant burns down the length of the tube like a cigarette.

Suppose we drill a hole all the way along the center line of the "grain" (that's what solid-rocket men call the propellant loaded into the "case"). Then if we flash an igniter jet down the length of this tunnel, the flame propagates in a radial direction, and will finally reach the outer wall at the very instant all the propellant is consumed. With the increasing diameter of the tunnel, the combustion surface increases. Consequently, the combustion gas produced per second, and the thrust generated by it, will be smallest at the moment of ignition and largest at the moment of burnout.

Usually a solid-propellant rocket is designed especially for a

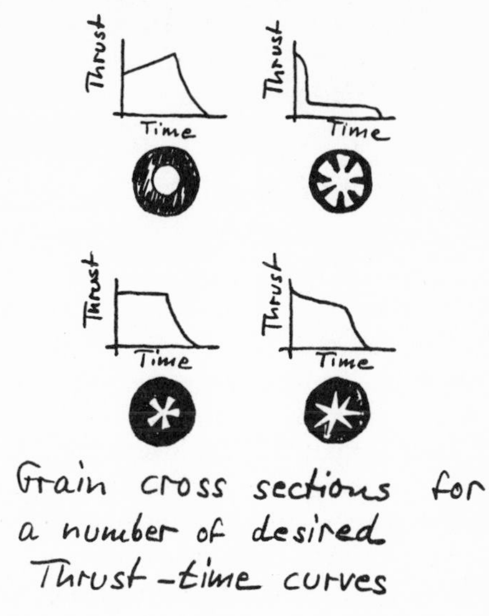

Grain cross sections for a number of desired Thrust-time curves

kind of performance most likely to be wanted. This means that there is a certain desired relationship between thrust and time. For instance, there may be a requirement to have the maximum thrust at takeoff, when the rocket is heavy, and to have the thrust taper off as it gets lighter. To meet such specifications, rocket designers have developed all kinds of sophisticated grain-cross sections, along which the flame front may proceed, to create the desired combustion surface at any given instant (see my sketch). Occasionally this method is further refined by the use of two or more layers of propellant with a different "linear burning rate"—the speed at which the flame front eats its way through the propellant, in inches per second.

Control of the rocket in flight can be accomplished in a variety of ways. Small ballistic, short-range "barrage" rockets are usually fin-stabilized like an arrow or spin-stabilized like a bullet. Larger medium, long-range, or antiaircraft rockets with sophisticated inertial or radio-guidance systems, however, need a suitable mechanism to convert the electrical steering signals into forces powerful enough to change the rocket's flight path. Aerodynamic control surfaces alone are usually not sufficient; they are ineffective right after takeoff, as well as in the vacuum of outer space. So flat jet

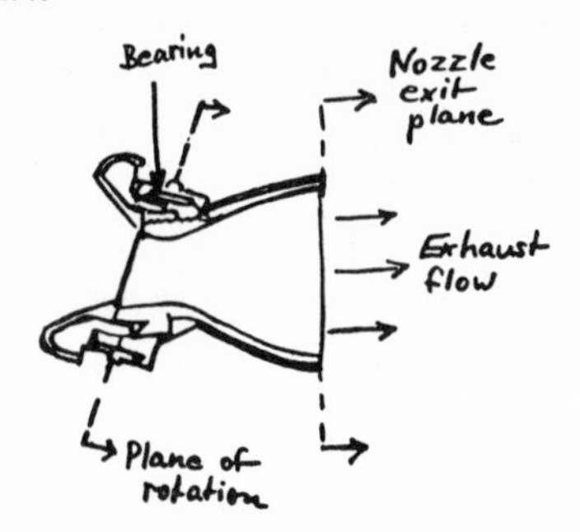

vanes or pivoted ring-shaped "jetavators," which can be tilted so as partially to deflect the jet from the nozzle, are often used.

Some of our large solid-propellant long-range ballistic rockets utilize several parallel nozzles through which the gases from the same rocket engine discharge. In this case, "thrust vector control" is often accomplished by rotating the nozzles. The plane of rotation of such a nozzle is skewed to the nozzle exit plane (see my sketch). The sealing and friction problems involved are easier to overcome than with tiltable nozzles.

Just as important as thrust vector control is the ability to shut off the rocket thrust of a ballistic rocket, after the necessary velocity for the desired range has been reached. This may be done by "thrust termination"—for instance, by blowing off the entire exhaust nozzle, so that the abrupt pressure drop extinguishes the fire. Another method uses "thrust reversal": A number of ports are opened, usually by blasting their membrane covers away. Some of the escaping exhaust gases discharge in the forward direction, with their total backward thrust exceeding the remaining forward thrust. Since the warhead is simultaneously released, this technique in effect backs the spent rocket away from the nose cone at the moment the desired speed is reached.

Casings of solid-propellant rockets are usually made of high-strength steel, titanium, or wound fiberglass.

A hybrid rocket is a crossbreed between a liquid-propellant and a solid-propellant rocket, in that it uses one liquid- and one solid-propellant component. Usually it has a solid-fuel grain against which a liquid oxidizer is sprayed. Sometimes the arrangement is the other way around.

Hybrid rockets offer a number of potential advantages. Their nozzles can be cooled by the liquid component, which may result in substantial weight savings over the heavy uncooled nozzles of long-burning solid-propellant rockets. Then, the thrust of a hybrid is easily controllable by throttling the liquid component. With the same throttling valve, the rocket can also be turned off completely and started again—the latter trick still being beyond the reach of any solid rocket.

Certain liquid components suitable for hybrid rockets—whether fuel or oxidizer—can also be used as monopropellants. (*See* Chapter 8. "How Propellants Are Fed to Liquid-Rocket Engines.) That is, on being fed through a suitable "catalyst bed," they decompose into a moderately hot gas. This feature can be used for numerous auxiliary purposes: tank pressurization, pneumatic-control pressure, attitude-control nozzles, vernier thrust for precise guidance maneuvers.

For all their potential, hybrid rockets still have failed to find much practical application. Many designers feel that they merely share the disadvantages of the low-energy solid-propellant rockets and the highly complex liquid-propellant rockets, and thus are not too attractive. Others believe that there will be applications in which the hybrid rocket will prevail.

How Propellants Are Fed to Liquid-Rocket Engines

Two basically different methods for feeding propellants into a liquid-rocket engine are in use: pressure feeding and pump feeding.

Pressure feeding is simple, but relatively heavy. Pump feeding offers a substantial weight advantage, at the price of greater complexity.

In a pressure-fed rocket-propulsion system, the fuel and oxidizer tanks are pressurized to a level sufficient to feed the propellants directly into the combustion chamber.

For efficiency, the combustion-chamber pressure must be pretty high—and the feed pressures obviously must be still higher. Thus, pressure-fed rockets require strong and heavy propellant tanks.

The main advantage of pressure feeding is simplicity. The inherent weight disadvantage becomes less noticeable in some rockets, such as air-defense missiles. Due to their high accelerations, and aerodynamic loads caused by maneuvering within the atmosphere, these rockets are subjected to high structural loads. The tanks that form their structure must be strong, anyhow.

The pressurizing gas for a pressure-fed rocket may simply be taken along in high-pressure containers. To save weight, some rockets carry the pressurizing gas in liquefied form. The liquid is converted into a gas either by heating it in a heat exchanger or by chemical decomposition.

In the latter case the liquid must be a "monopropellant." This is a chemical that decomposes into its components, and simultaneously releases heat, on contact with a suitable catalyst. Hydrogen peroxide (H_2O_2), a water-like liquid, decomposes into a mixture of steam (H_2O) and oxygen (O_2) when forced through a catalyst bed of calcium permanganate. Another monopropellant, hydrazine (N_2H_4), which is likewise liquid at room temperature, decomposes on contact with a catalyst into a mixture of hot nitrogen (N_2) and hydrogen (H_2) gases.

Solid propellants are rarely used to generate pressurizing gas for pressure-fed liquid rockets, since all of them produce quantities of solid particles in the gas, which may clog valves or regulators and may also be corrosive. Liquids injected into the tanks to react chemically with the fuel or oxidizer in order to produce a pressurizing gas are likewise not popular because of inherent hazards and several undesirable side effects.

My sketch shows the principle of a typical pressure-fed liquid rocket.

Because of the substantial weight advantage, virtually all high-performance liquid-propellant rockets use pump feeding. It permits using thin lightweight propellant containers in combination with highly efficient high-pressure rocket engines.

There are always two separate pumps—one for the fuel, the other for the oxidizer. Most common are centrifugal pumps, not too different in basic design from the water pumps used in fire engines. For liquid hydrogen, however, multibladed axial pumps are often used. Their rotors look a bit like the compressors of turbojet engines.

The propellant pumps of all liquid rockets are powered by gas turbines. Sometimes the pumps are mounted on a common shaft with the drive turbine either between the two pumps or on one end.

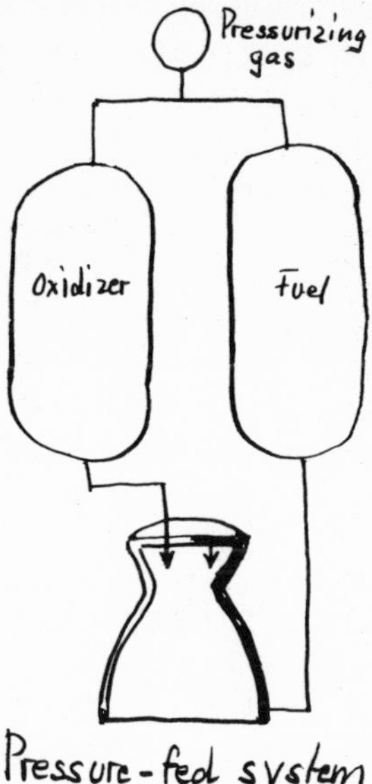

Pressure-fed system

Sometimes the high-r.p.m. turbine is connected to the slower-spinning pumps via a gear train. In some rocket engines the pumps are separate, each with its own turbine.

The turbines are always driven by expansion of hot high-pressure gas through their blades. But many different methods have been developed to generate the drive gas.

Early liquid rockets, such as the V-2, Viking, and Redstone, used a *monopropellant* gas source and carried a separate hydrogen peroxide container. From this relatively small tank, the peroxide was pressure-fed into a catalytic decomposition chamber. Steam and oxygen emerging from this chamber drove the turbine.

Most modern liquid-rocket engines use *bipropellant* gas generators. Oxidizer and fuel are tapped off the high-pressure discharge lines of their respective pumps and are fed into a gas generator. This is a high-pressure furnace in which the propellants burn—usually at a rather fuel-rich mixture ratio, to keep the gas temperature low enough for the turbine blades.

In the 200,000-pound-thrust Rocketdyne J-2 engine—the liquid-hydrogen/liquid-oxygen engine that will power the second and third stages of the Saturn V moon rocket—the hydrogen-rich

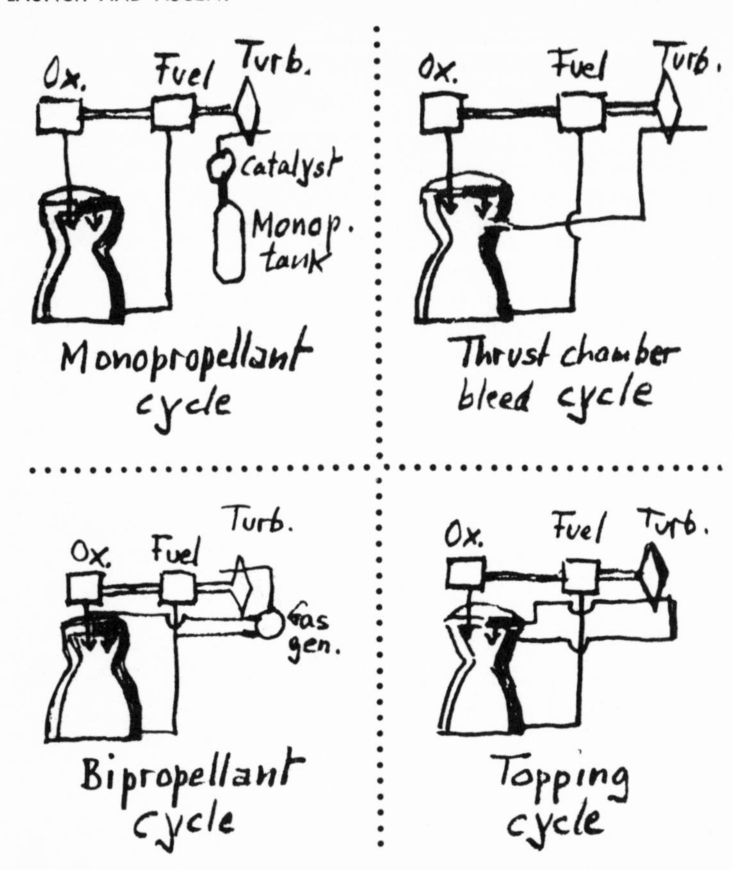

combustion gas emerging from the gas generator first drives the turbine of the liquid-hydrogen pump. Still rather hot and under moderate pressure, the gas is then ducted to the opposite side of the engine, where its further expansion drives the turbine of the liquid-oxygen pump. Through a large wraparound manifold, the cooled-off drive gas is finally admitted to the rocket's main exhaust nozzle, where it augments the thrust.

Of course, only a minute fraction of the fuel and oxidizer is tapped off into the gas generator. The bulk flows into the main combustion chamber.

Instead of producing the turbine drive gas in a separate gas generator, it has been repeatedly attempted to bleed the gas directly off the main combustion chamber. While this *thrust-chamber bleed cycle* looks at first blush like a very obvious solution, it poses two major difficulties. For one, the gas bled off the main chamber after the combustion process has been completed, is too hot to be admitted directly to the turbine. It must either be tapped off at a point where combustion is still incomplete, or it must be cooled by injection of water or additional fuel. Secondly, it is quite difficult to control the power level of the turbine with sufficient accuracy, because the heat energy of the drive gas is greatly dependent upon the local gas condition in the chamber near the bleed-off point. Nevertheless, rocket engine designers are quite optimistic that both problems can be solved by a strategic location and distribution of tap-off points.

The so-called *topping cycle* provides the best turbine-drive system from the viewpoint of operational advantages and overall economy as long as the combustion pressure in the main chamber is kept moderate. This cycle is used in the Pratt & Whitney RL-10 hydrogen-oxygen engine, six of which power the second stage of the Saturn I rocket.

In the topping cycle, the liquid hydrogen is pumped through the cooling jacket of the main combustion chamber, where it picks up enough heat from the warm metal to evaporate. Led through the turbine, the expanding gas spins it. The expanded hydrogen is then admitted to the combustion chamber, where it burns with the oxygen that has been pumped in separately.

The older pump-fed rockets, using a monopropellant gas generator, were started by first establishing a small gravity-fed flow of fuel and oxidizer into the combustion chamber, and igniting it. Then the hydrogen peroxide valve was opened, admitting the pressure-fed stream of monopropellant to the catalyst bed. The vapor emerging from the gas generator whipped the turbine up to speed, and the rocket took off.

Rocket engines with bipropellant gas generators are usually started with pyrotechnic "spinners." A little solid-propellant "rocket" shoots a fire stream simultaneously into the turbine blades and into the gas generator. Ignition of fuel and oxidizer entering the gas generator is provided by the spinner flame. After the spinner extinguishes, the pumps keep running.

Topping-cycle engines burning liquid hydrogen are the easiest to start. One simply opens a valve, allowing liquid hydrogen to flow by gravity into the warm cooling jacket. As the cold liquid absorbs heat and evaporates, the expanding gas starts to spin the turbopump. This increases the flow rate of the liquid hydrogen into the cooling jacket, which, in turn, further increases the gas flow through the turbine.

The topping cycle thus takes ingenious advantage of the allegedly hard-to-handle "cryogenic" fuels (low-boiling liquefied gases such as liquid hydrogen): It uses the temperature difference between the room-temperature engine metal and the cold propellant to start the engine.

Pump-fed engines can be throttled quite easily. It's done by throttling the r.p.m. of the turbopump.

With monopropellant gas generators, one simply throttles the flow of monopropellant to the catalyst bed. The resulting r.p.m. drop of the turbine reduces the flow rates of fuel and oxidizer and, thus, the combustion pressure and engine thrust.

In a bipropellant system, the same effect is obtained by throttling the flows of both propellants into the gas generator.

The hydrogen-oxygen topping-cycle engine is throttled by increasing a variable percentage of hydrogen, emerging from the cooling jacket, that is allowed to bypass the turbine and enter the thrust chamber directly. Likewise, a drop in turbine r.p.m. results.

The control of mixture ratio is a critical problem, particularly with large and highly efficient liquid-rocket systems. Obviously, all advantages gained by ultra-light structural design could easily be lost if the control of the mixture ratio was so poor that thousands of pounds of useless oxygen were left in the rocket's tanks when the fuel was used up.

Modern large liquid rockets often have "capacity probes," inserted in the fuel and oxidizer tanks, that indicate at every moment how much there is left in each tank. This information is fed into a simple computer that controls a throttle or bypass valve in either the fuel or the oxidizer system. The throttle valve then sees to it that both propellants are depleted simultaneously. Such "propellant-utilization systems" even permit rocket engines to be operated at varying mixture ratios during flight—which turns out to be advantageous for squeezing maximum payload performance out of a rocket of given design.

There are two reasons why liquid hydrogen is such a good rocket fuel. One is the high heat energy released by the combustion of hydrogen. The other, equally important but less obvious, is the low molecular weight of hydrogen and its combustion product, water vapor.

The exhaust velocity of a rocket engine is the best yardstick of its fuel economy. Each gas molecule spurting from a rocket motor's exhaust nozzle can be looked upon as a tiny bullet fired from a gun. The higher the muzzle velocity, the more recoil will be exerted on the gun barrel. As the thrust of a rocket motor is made up of the total of all the little recoils produced by millions of molecule bullets, and the exhaust gas is produced by burning fuel, it follows that the higher the exhaust velocity with a given amount of fuel, the greater will be the rocket motor's thrust.

The exhaust nozzle of a rocket motor can be looked upon as a device that orients the all-directional movement of the gas molecules in the combustion chamber into one predominant direction. The exhaust velocity is, therefore, directly related to the velocity at which the gases whirl around in the chamber immediately after combustion but prior to entering the exhaust nozzle.

Now a fundamental law of physics states that *at a given temperature the average kinetic energy of the whirling molecules of any two gases must be the same.* The kinetic energy, or energy of motion of a body, depends on two factors: its weight (or mass) and its speed. This means that in order for a light and a heavy body to have the same kinetic energy, the light one must be faster. It follows that for a given combustion temperature in a rocket engine, the propellant combination that produces lighter exhaust products will also produce a higher exhaust velocity.

Of course, a high combustion energy is needed to obtain a high combustion temperature. The combustion of hydrogen is one of the most powerful reactions known in chemistry. But, as we have seen, a light combustion product with a low average molecular weight is equally important. Hydrogen, with a molecular weight of only 2, is the lightest gas in existence. Even its combustion product, water vapor, resulting from reaction between two hydrogen atoms and one oxygen atom, has a molecular weight of only 18, which is quite low compared with that of combustion products of other fuels. Moreover, rocket engines using liquid hydrogen as fuel and liquid oxygen as oxidizer operate at maximum efficiency when running at a fuel-rich mixture. This means there are more hydrogen atoms around than there are oxygen atoms available with which they could react. The exhaust jet of such a rocket engine is therefore composed of a mixture of water vapor and unburned hydrogen, with a molecular weight somewhere between 18 and 2. It is because of these advantages that rocket engineers put great faith in liquid hydrogen.

Rocket-riding Cameras Show How Boosters Behave

On the morning of January 29, 1964, our fifth Saturn I roared into orbit from Pad 37-B at Cape Kennedy, Florida. Less than an hour after takeoff, the first of eight motion-picture-camera capsules, ejected from the first stage after burnout, were recovered from the sea some 550 miles downrange. Paradivers dropped from planes into the rough water, inflated their rafts, and hauled five of the capsules aboard. Two capsules that could not be retrieved before dark, due to high winds and waves up to ten feet, were salvaged by a recovery ship guided by flares from the aircraft.

When the seventh Saturn I was launched on September 18, 1964, Hurricane Gladys kicked up fifteen-foot waves in the capsule's impact area and all attempts to recover them were canceled. However, on November 9th, two of the capsules were discovered by beachcombers. One had washed ashore on San Salvador Island, the other on Eleuthera. A third capsule was recovered April 1965 by a swimmer off San Salvador. Despite the battering the capsules took, most of the recovered films furnished useful information.

Because camera capsules enable a designer actually to see what happens in flight, they are proving invaluable in developing rocket launch vehicles. They offer important advantages over other means, such as telemetry, of reporting a rocket's behavior.

The ejectable motion-picture-camera capsule for the Saturn was developed and tested by scientists and engineers of NASA's Marshall Space Flight Center, supported by the Cook Technological Center in Chicago. The capsule weighs about 60 pounds, has a diameter of 7¾ inches, and is 28½ inches long. There are two different types:

The so-called Model A capsule serves for "direct viewing." It films events visible from the camera's position before its ejection. At its forward end is a quartz viewing window that protects the camera lens from aerodynamic heating. Four such direct-viewing cameras, mounted on the front end of the first stage and looking forward, photograph the second stage's igniting and thrusting away from the first one.

The Model B capsule employs "indirect viewing." The camera lens looks into a "fiber-optics bundle"—to all intents, a flexible metallic hose that permits optical images to be piped around corners. The opposite end of the fiber-optics bundle may be connected, for instance, to the upper bulkhead of the liquid-oxygen tank. The camera capsule then looks into the pressurized tank, just as if you were peering into a container whose lid has been removed. A special incandescent lamp provides enough light to film events inside the tank.

A cutaway view of the recoverable camera capsule, 28½ inches in length. This direct-viewing model has a quartz window to protect the camera from the heat of high-speed flight through the atmosphere.

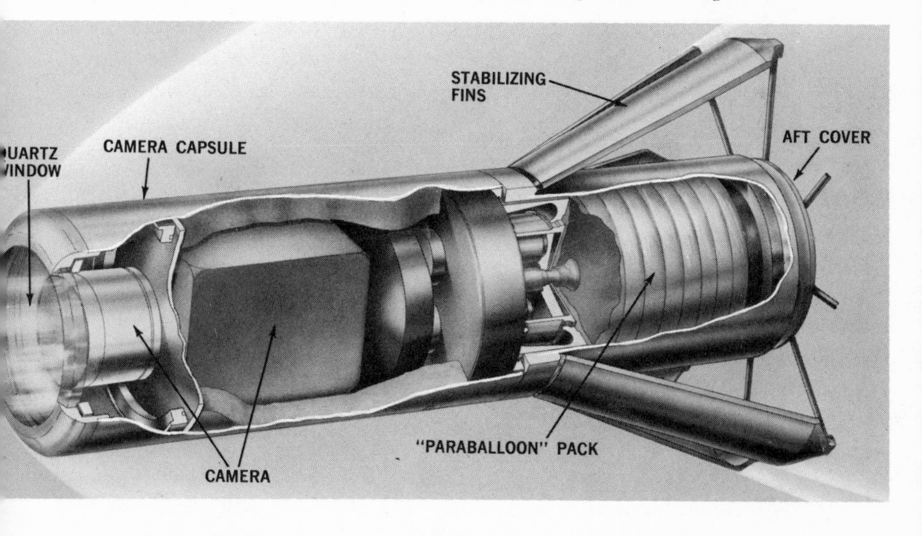

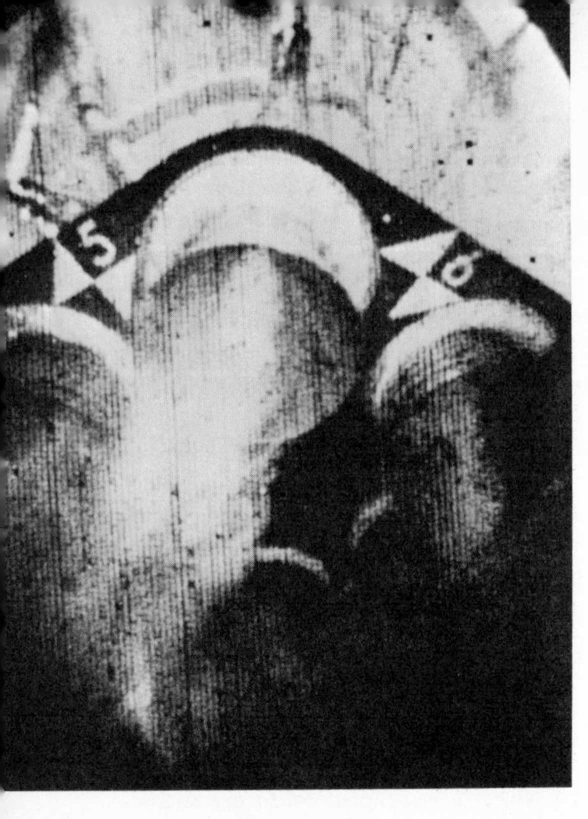

A photo of the ignition of second-stage engines of a Saturn I. Photo was made and brought back by the camera capsule.

Essentially the fiber-optics bundle consists of several thousand glass fibers, each about as thick as ordinary knitting yarn. The body of each glass fiber is transparent; its surface is mirror-coated. Therefore, a light beam entering the fiber at one end will be mirrored down the fiber and emerge at the other end, no matter how the fiber is bent or twisted. So, when an optical image is cast on a raster of thousands of front ends of parallel-bundled fibers, the same image will appear on a raster of correspondingly oriented rear ends.

The capsules are ejected when the Saturn I booster is traveling at about 8,400 feet per second (roughly, 5,700 m.p.h.). This is done by catapulting the capsule out of a tube, with the help of pressurizing nitrogen gas. Immediately on leaving the catapult tube, the capsule extends spring-loaded flaps for aerodynamic stabilization.

Each capsule contains a "paraballoon"—an inflatable sphere, with a parachute-like drag skirt attached. At an altitude of 14,000 feet, an aneroid switch causes the bladder of the paraballoon to inflate with pressurized nitrogen. The expanding bladder's pressure, severing shear screws, detaches the entire aft cover (including the stabilizing fins) from the capsule.

Continuing to inflate, the paraballoon reaches its full 18-inch diameter. The combined drag of balloon and skirt slows the falling capsule to a terminal velocity of about 100 feet per second (68 m.p.h.), the speed at which it strikes the water. The inflated paraballoon provides enough buoyancy to keep the capsule afloat.

Why are recovered film capsules so valuable? The answer is found in the fundamental difficulties faced by every rocket designer.

A developer of a new aircraft can learn how his brainchild behaves and handles from the test pilot. Built-in flight recorders provide further data. And test flights can be repeated, barring a serious accident, until both the designer and the test pilot are happy with the results.

A developer of a space-launch vehicle is in a less enviable position. His large rockets cannot be flown back to base. While his vehicles are still in the experimental stage, he must equip them with artificial eyes and ears—and see to it that he can evaluate, on the ground, what those eyes and ears see and hear during a flight.

The traditional way to get data in flight has been telemetry. But radioing such information as pressures, temperatures, and voltages to the ground has limitations.

During the development of the Saturn I launch vehicle, for instance, we wanted to know how the second-stage engines ignited, and how the second stage separated from the spent first stage. We wanted to find out, too, whether or not the first stage's oxygen tanks were properly designed to permit complete emptying. Did a vortex, such as you see when a bathtub drains, let pressurizing gas enter the liquid-oxygen feed line prematurely—before the liquid level neared the bottom of the tank? Telemetry is not too well suited to answer such questions. It takes artificial eyes to see what goes on in stage separation—and whether a vortex develops in that LOX tank.

In some cases rocket designers have successfully used small television cameras—but this has limitations, too. During the stage-separation sequence, small solid "retrorockets" retard the exhausted first stage, the second-stage engines are ignited while small solid "ullage rockets" settle the liquid propellants on their tank bottoms. These fire-spitting operations interfere with telemetry or TV communication between rocket and ground at this vital phase of a flight.

It is in such situations that ejectable motion-picture-camera capsules prove their worth—and justify the effort needed to find them and fish them from the sea.

To help in locating and retrieving it, a camera capsule provides these built-in recovery aids:

A small radio beacon on the upper part of the paraballoon enables aircraft and ships to home in on the floating capsule.

A high-intensity light beacon, flashing twenty times a minute, aids night recovery.

A dye marker colors the surrounding water green with a fluorescein dye—an aid of proven value for daylight recovery.

The painted pattern of the paraballoon contributes to safe recovery. Alternating white and day-glow orange panels, above the waterline, give high visibility. The hemisphere below the waterline is a dark purple, to be least attractive to nosy fish.

A shark repellent of proven effectiveness, cupric acetate, is released into the surrounding water. It prevents the paraballoon—and the paradiver recovering it—from ending up in a shark's stomach.

What Happens to a Rocket Booster?

Viewed at night, the burn-up of a rocket booster is a spectacular sight. And the man-made shooting star offers observers an unusual chance to study the phenomena of high-speed re-entry, newly important in this space age.

What happens to a spent booster is an interesting and revealing story. It has many different versions, because of the widely varying velocities at which the re-entry of rocket boosters takes place.

To the best of my knowledge, the U.S. Army's 200-mile Redstone ballistic rocket was the first missile ever to feature separation of the booster from the warhead in flight. For shorter-range missiles that would be an unnecessary complication and would risk dropping spent stages on friendly troops. Even the German 200-mile V-2 ballistic rocket had no provision for booster separation;

its resulting simplification was bought at the price of a rather heavy steel hull for the entire missile, to enable it to withstand the substantial pressure and heat that it encountered during re-entry.

The booster of the Redstone separates as the boost phase ends and unpowered flight in a ballistic trajectory begins. At power cut-off, a Redstone going for maximum range is speeding at about 3,500 m.p.h., has an angle of elevation of some 40 degrees, and has reached about 25-mile altitude.

Under these conditions, aerodynamic drag on the spent and detached booster is quite small, and it becomes totally negligible in about ten seconds' more climbing. The booster tumbles slowly—at a rate depending on the lack of symmetry of the kick at separation—as it trails the payload up to the sixty-mile-high top of the parabola-shaped trajectory, and then back toward earth.

Some twenty miles short of the 200-mile target, the Redstone's warhead, and the tumbling booster trailing a few hundred feet behind, re-enter the denser layers of the atmosphere. The warhead's nose is kept pointing in the direction of the flight path by a jet-nozzle attitude-control system. Streamlined, arrow-stable, and thus plunging rapidly, the heavy warhead is precisely guided to the target by its inertial-guidance system, which acts on a set of movable air vanes in the warhead's tail.

In contrast, the empty booster, lightweight and tumbling, slows down fast. In less than a minute after re-entry begins, its forward speed drops to zero, and its rate of descent to well below the speed of sound. Its end-over-end motion averts excessive aerodynamic heating of any particular spot, and the pressure left in the propellant tanks keeps it from collapsing under the considerable aerodynamic loads. Not weak enough to break up, the booster continues falling toward earth.

The velocity of the booster at impact—on water, in missile-range firings—may vary between 200 and 400 feet per second (about 135 to 270 m.p.h.). How the booster will strike the water—endwise or broadside—is unpredictable, as it does not assume a steady position in falling.

Boosters have often been found floating in the ocean after impact. While their propellant tanks had not sprung a leak that would sink them, vital parts were so badly damaged that repair and re-use of the boosters was out of the question.

Deploying a parachute before impact would be possible. And drop and seawater-submergence tests have demonstrated the possibility of re-using such elements as the rocket engine. Even so, it is not very likely that boosters recovered from the sea will ever be an answer to our search for economical, re-usable boosters. Recovery and refurbishment of ocean-landed boosters would be costly and involved. More important, the reliability that can be expected of an ocean-recovered rocket will always fall short of that of a fresh-from-the-factory rocket that has passed a tight screen of quality-control inspectors en route. Comparable reliability can be foreseen only from future boosters that can fly back to base under their own power. (*See* page 85, "Coming . . . Ferries to Space.")

For longer-range rocket missiles than Redstone, higher initial velocities are required. Resulting re-entry speeds are likewise higher. An Intermediate Range Ballistic Missile (IRBM) such as the U.S. Air Force's 1,500-nautical-mile Thor or Jupiter has a re-entry velocity in the neighborhood of 15,000 feet per second (about 10,000 m.p.h.).

At such speeds, booster separation no longer is an option available to a designer who wants to gain a little extra missile range, but becomes a *must*. To survive the blazing high-speed re-entry, the warhead must be provided with a special heat shield. Extending this shield over the booster's tankage would make it prohibitively heavy, and would be pointless, since it would not contribute one iota of effect on the target. Thor and Jupiter boosters were therefore detached at booster cutoff and permitted to burn up during re-entry.

In 1958, to learn more about the phenomena of high-speed re-entry, the path of the descending Jupiter IRBM—then still experimental—came under special study. Some fifty miles uprange from the predicted impact point, a Navy-assigned destroyer provided a grandstand view, and cameras and a spectrograph were trained upon the spectacle.

Visible for about twenty-four seconds, the meteor-like display perceptibly illuminated the distant ship. The burning aluminum tankage of the booster produced, as expected, a brilliant streak across the night sky—many times brighter than the brightest star

Re-entry of Jupiter missile, viewed from the island of Antigua, makes shooting-star display. The brightest streak is the falling booster; other luminous trails are of the instrument compartment and nose cone.

and, also, far more brilliant than the luminous trail of the warhead preceding it.

Next morning, however, for all this celestial display, some innards of Jupiter boosters such as compressed-nitrogen bottles and small electrical parts were found floating in the water. Analysis of these parts gave a blow-by-blow account of what happens when a re-entering booster burns up.

At first, only the booster's outside is exposed to aerodynamic pressure and heating. It takes a while to break or burn up the external surfaces—made up of pressurized propellant tankage and skin structures such as the guidance compartment and the tail structure around the rocket engine. Only then will the booster's interior be exposed to the searing and blazing air stream. And small parts inside the hull may still be shielded from the blaze by additional protective layers.

Take, for instance, the armature of an electric motor within an aluminum "black box," which may also hold other elements of the missile's electrical system. The "black box" undergoes aerodynamic heating only after the surrounding guidance compartment is consumed—which will take much of the total time required to slow the disintegrating vehicle. Heating and melting the aluminum "black box" takes more time—and so, in turn, does the destruction of the motor casing that still shields the armature within it. So the armature may not be exposed to the onrushing air until the booster is moving too slowly for aerodynamic heating to be effective—and may thus survive re-entry without damage.

For boosters of space vehicles, the story is much like that of boosters of short- and intermediate-range missiles. Boosters of two or three stages hurl spacecraft into orbit or beyond—and the various stages drop off at velocities more or less comparable with Redstone and Jupiter separation speeds. One notable exception is the Atlas booster, in the configuration used for the Atlas-Mercury orbital flights.

The Atlas rocket does not use "conventional" staging—in which complete rocket stages, including tanks and rocket engines, are dropped off to save weight. Instead, it uses "engine staging." Two "booster" engines are dropped off during ascent, and the flight continues under the power of one "sustainer" engine fed from the same propellant tanks. Thus the re-entry phenomena that we have been discussing apply only to the detached "booster" engines.

The Atlas' entire tankage is carried into orbit. The orbits attained in Atlas-Mercury flights were only about a hundred miles up, and decayed after two or three orbits. Since Atlas tankage is made of steel, its chance of surviving re-entry was much higher than that of the aluminum tankage used in most boosters. Parts of Atlas tankage stemming from Mercury flights have indeed been found in Latin America.

II. FLIGHT THROUGH SPACE

Why a Satellite Stays Up and How It Comes Down

Have you wondered what makes a satellite go into an orbit? Well, imagine yourself standing on a high mountain peak, well above the atmosphere, firing a gun in a horizontal direction. (See my sketch.) The shell, after leaving the gun barrel, will first fly horizontally. But soon the earth's gravitational pull bends the trajectory downward, as in the shortest of the paths in the sketch.

Reload the gun with a more powerful charge and the shell will fly farther, as shown by the next-longer path in the sketch. Its trajectory will be less deflected because the centrifugal force (as it follows the earth's curvature) is increased by its higher speed, and more effectively counteracts the earth's gravitational pull.

If you could use a charge powerful enough to give your shell a velocity of about 4.9 miles a second (17,600 m.p.h.), *the curvature of the downward-bent trajectory would become equal to the curvature of the earth.* The shell would keep flying and flying, and about 85 minutes later you'd better take cover—because the projectile, having gone all the way around the earth, would approach you from behind and hit the breech of the gun in the rear. The shell would have traveled in a circular orbit, the longest and globe-circling path in my sketch. If you don't believe it, ask John

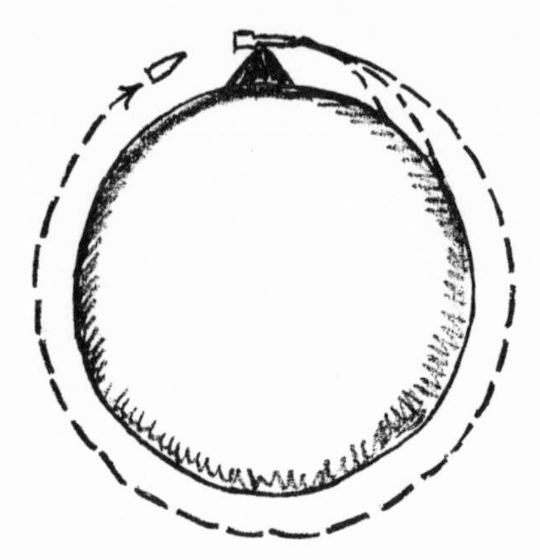

Glenn, Scott Carpenter, Wally Schirra, Gordon Cooper, or any of our other astronauts.

In more general terms, this is what makes an orbit tick, and decides what kind of an orbit it will be:

A *circular* orbit occurs whenever a small mass, traveling through the gravitational field of a big one, happens to have a speed at which the centrifugal force is precisely strong enough to balance the large body's gravitational pull. This precision exists, to a high degree, in the orbiting of the moon around the earth and of the earth and Venus around the sun.

If the balance between gravitational and centrifugal force is not perfect, but the centrifugal force is strong enough to prevent a direct collision, the small body will describe an *elliptical* path around the large one. Comets follow elliptical orbits around the sun.

The second of my sketches sums up the conditions that will give rise to a circular or elliptical orbit, respectively.

A synchronous satellite (such as our Early Bird, Telstar, and Syncom communications satellites) is a space craft coasting from west to east in a very high circular orbit, with a period of revolution of exactly twenty-four hours. An additional requirement is that the plane of the orbit must coincide, at least fairly nearly, with the plane of the equator.

Since the earth likewise revolves about its axis from west to east once every twenty-four hours, and since the earth's axis is at right angles to the plane of the equator, a synchronous satellite appears to stand still forever—directly above one particular spot on

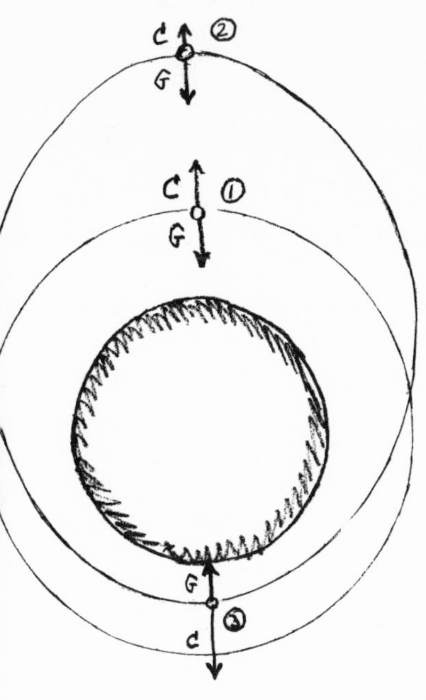

the equator. (Or if it has been launched on a path somewhat inclined to the equator, as in the case of Syncom No. 2, it appears to move back and forth with a figure-8 motion above such a spot. As is required for a twenty-four-hour period of revolution, its height is always 22,300 miles above the earth's surface.

Synchronous satellites are of great interest for global communications. Because of its great distance from earth (about six earth radii), a twenty-four-hour satellite is simultaneously visible from a vast portion of the globe. For example, a Syncom satellite "hovering" above the Amazon delta in Brazil is in direct line-of-sight contact with places as far apart as Seattle, Thule (in Greenland), London, Rome, Cape Town, Buenos Aires, Los Angeles, and parts of Antarctica. It serves as a permanent telephone or television relay station, linking North America to Europe, Africa, and Latin America.

Such a communications service uses microwaves—which are beamed up to the synchronous satellite with the help of huge ground-based dish or horn antennas. The satellite itself need not have a directional antenna. It simply feeds the received signal into a solar-powered transmitter, and retransmits the amplified signal back to earth on a different frequency.

Microwaves permit the use of a great number of adjacent frequencies, without cross talk. Thus, a single synchronous satellite can handle many simultaneous telephone conversations and television programs.

Three synchronous communications satellites in the same orbit, spaced 120 degrees apart, can cover the entire earth (except for the areas around the North and South Poles, where all three satellites would be a trifle below the horizon).

Due to the satellites' enormous altitude, the travel time of the electronic signals from the earth's surface to the satellite and back amounts to almost one-third of a second. While this is immaterial for television, the time lag is quite noticeable in telephone conversations.

You may also have wondered why the capsules in which our Mercury and Gemini astronauts returned to earth were designed with a blunt nose.

For an orbiting spacecraft to return to the earth's surface, its initial velocity must be reduced to zero. To provide the entire retardation energy with retrorockets is unattractive; it would call for a rocket-propulsion system of about the same power and propellant consumption as the one used to carry the spacecraft into orbit in the first place. For this reason, retrorockets are employed only for the limited task of pushing the spacecraft's orbital path back into the atmosphere. The bulk of the braking action is provided by the ensuing aerodynamic drag. The drag is produced by air compression and air friction. Both generate heat. Suppose the kinetic energy of an iron ball, entering the atmosphere at an orbital speed of 25,600 feet per second, was completely converted into heat and all that heat was transferred back into the ball. It would never reach the ground, because there would be enough heat to melt thirty-five iron balls!

For successful re-entry it is therefore essential that only a small fraction of the total heat generated during aerodynamic deceleration be absorbed by the spacecraft. The most effective mechanism to carry energy away from the spacecraft and into the surrounding air is a shock wave. You may have witnessed the havoc caused to adjacent moorings by a large boat moving through a narrow channel at excessive speed. It demonstrates vividly that a very substantial portion of the boat's horsepower is carried away by the bow wave.

The blunter the bow, the stronger the wave. This is just as true for a spacecraft returning at hypersonic speeds.

We see, therefore, that the Mercury and Gemini capsules had a blunt nose in order to *minimize* the heat absorbed by the spacecraft's structure, and to *maximize* the heat carried away by the shock wave.

Supersonic airplanes are needle-nosed to keep down aerodynamic drag. This is necessary when the designer has the task of reaching ever-increasing speeds with the limited engine power at his disposal.

Aerodynamic heating, on the other hand, does not pose a very serious materials problem at the speeds of present-day supersonic aircraft, operating for very short periods at Mach 2 or 3.

An orbiting spacecraft such as the Mercury or Gemini capsule is boosted into space by a powerful rocket that rises vertically. Its flight path begins to level off only after it has cleared the denser layers of the atmosphere. Here, drag reduction during the ascent becomes a minor consideration. Re-entry from orbit, however, is commenced at Mach 25! During the blazing retardation maneuver that follows, the job of keeping the heat away from the capsule, and of dissipating as much of it as possible into the surrounding atmosphere, must be our first concern.

The Strange World of Zero Gravity

When, during a "space walk," an astronaut becomes a human satellite, floating freely in the vastness of space, he offers a dramatic example of the weird things that can happen in the realm of zero gravity.

In the Soviet space flight of March 1965, Lt. Col. Alexei Leonov left his orbiting Voskhov 2 spacecraft and sailed along beside it for ten minutes, at nearly 18,000 m.p.h., before returning along his trailing lifeline.

His eerie experience was shared, within only a few months, by our own spacemen. In June, 1965, Astronaut Edward H. White II emerged from his Gemini 4 capsule and demonstrated the feasibility of a controlled "spacewalk" with the aid of a hand-held reaction gun. In subsequent flights, Astronauts Cernan (Gemini 9), Collins (Gemini 10), and Gordon (Gemini 11) tackled the task of performing jobs of varying complexity outside their spacecraft. They encountered some difficulties and returned with the concensus that an extravehicular astronaut must be provided with adequate hand and footholds or other suitable methods to anchor himself in front of his work station if he is to do an effective job.

Subject to this strange environment of zero gravity is any spacecraft coasting unpowered through space—around the earth, or on the way to the moon or a planet. Inside the craft, as well as out, space voyagers find the familiar law of gravity apparently repealed. Any loose objects, astronauts included, will float about instead of staying put in seats or receptacles.

Actually, zero gravity or weightlessness does not mean at all that gravity has ceased to operate. It results, rather, from a situation where both the spacecraft and its contents can freely follow the identical forces of gravity. Once a spacecraft has been "injected" into any kind of unpowered trajectory in a vacuum, its hull, its crew, and its contents will faithfully obey the laws of motion governing all heavenly bodies—and so, there can be no relative forces between them. Living and housekeeping under zero gravity, therefore, pose curious problems:

Before going to sleep, astronauts strap themselves down, or they float about the cabin, propelled by the thrust of their own breaths.

Sponge baths, rather than showers, must be the style for bathing under zero gravity.

Like babies, astronauts must drink from squeezable plastic bottles. If a spaceman tried to get water out of an ordinary bottle, it would be like the problem you encounter when you try to pour catsup on your hamburger—first you get none, then more than you want.

For short trips, food for astronauts is taken along in dehydrated form. Water is injected into the plastic food bag and, after a bit of kneading, the astronaut squeezes the resulting creamy substance into his mouth by pulling the bag through his closed teeth.

It is interesting to note that astronauts have no difficulty in swallowing under zero-gravity conditions. The esophagus is equipped with a series of ring muscles that force the food down to the stomach, regardless of the presence or absence of gravity. This action is so effective that it even works *against* gravity: you can eat while standing on your head!

As the duration of future space flights will increase, more comfortable ways of eating will be provided. As a minimum, astronauts will want warm food of the "add water, heat, and serve" type.

For planetary voyages lasting several hundred days, you can rest assured that it will be shrimp cocktail, filet mignon, Waldorf salad —the works. Spacecraft pantries will have more or less conventional deep-freeze compartments, infrared broilers, coffee dispensers, and spice cabinets. Even the most luxurious space cuisine for long-duration voyages, however, will avoid needless food wastes. All meat will be boneless and free of undesirable fat; potatoes will be peeled in advance; cherries will be stoneless. If a Martini is ever served aboard a spacecraft, it may come without an olive.

Ingenuity will be required of designers of tableware for gracious dining under zero gravity. Dishes will need spring-loaded covers so a steak won't float away. And, of course, the dishes themselves must somehow be anchored. Forks are fine, but spoons are useless. Knives either will use saw action to minimize cutting pressure, or will be replaced by scissors-type devices that can do without any one-sided pressure.

Tools for use under zero gravity will have special designs, too. If a weightless astronaut tried to tighten a nut with an ordinary wrench, the effort would only spin him around. Instead, he'll use a "squeeze wrench" that does not require a firm foothold to apply a twist.

Cleanliness is the key to good housekeeping, in space as at home. And, under zero gravity, rigorous cleanliness is even more important than at home. Once up in orbit and under zero-gravity conditions, any dust or dirt in a spacecraft would not harmlessly settle under a chair or on a rug. It would float around—and could be inhaled, or short-circuit electrical terminals, or be sucked into the air-conditioning system. That's one good reason why zwieback wouldn't be popular in a spacecraft.

The spacecraft is assembled and checked out under "white-room conditions" comparable to the cleanliness standards of a hospital operating room. Even when perched on top of the huge launch rocket prior to takeoff, it is accessible only through a servicing room operated under white-room standards. After the astronauts leave their specially equipped Transfer Van, they ride up in a spic-and-span elevator to that servicing room, located on the top floor of the gantry. Before entering the spacecraft they remove special shoe covers. All these precautions are to prevent any dirt or dust from getting into the craft.

Any loose tools or pieces of special equipment used within the spacecraft must have their proper storage spaces or tie-up straps. A monkey wrench, harmlessly floating in a corner of a spacecraft for weeks of zero gravity, can turn into a deadly missile the moment the rocket engines are turned on or the decelerated re-entry into the atmosphere begins.

So far we have discussed zero-gravity problems that can be foreseen quite clearly. We cannot yet speak with equal assurance about the most important one of all.

A great deal has been written and speculated about man's ability to live and perform under zero gravity over extended periods of time. Prior to the first manned orbital flight, this was indeed a matter of gravest concern. To date, we know this much:

Our Mercury and Gemini astronauts have experienced many hours of weightlessness in their orbital flights. In February, 1962, John Glenn came home after three orbits and said that extended weightlessness was an exhilarating experience and did not effect his piloting proficiency at all. Leroy Gordon Cooper, who circled the earth for more than thirty-four hours on May 15th and 16th in 1963, performed a brilliant manual re-entry maneuver at the end of his twenty-two-orbit flight—demonstrating convincingly that even after this much longer exposure to zero gravity his effectiveness and precision had not suffered one bit. In December, 1965, Frank Borman and James Lovell stayed in orbit for no less than two weeks in their Gemini 7 and came back in fine shape and high spirits. They clearly proved that our forthcoming Apollo flights to the moon and back, which will last approximately ten days, are not likely to run into unpleasant surprises caused by weightlessness en route.

Nevertheless, it would be rash to say that extended zero gravity could pose no serious physiological problems. Both interplanetary voyages and extended earth-orbital operations for scientific research or earth-oriented activities will involve exposures to weightlessness over much longer periods. Only time and experience will tell whether or not man is adaptable enough to continue to perform with dispatch and precision. It may well be that for such an extended operation we must take recourse to artificial gravity produced by spin-induced centrifugal force. Meanwhile, we can assume that, to retain their physical fitness during extended space flights, astronauts will need equipment for regular physical exercise —and this will be easy to provide. Sporting-goods stores are full of exercisers, ranging from simple stretch belts to elaborate rowing and pedaling machines, that lend themselves well to use under zero gravity in outer space.

Artificial Gravity

On September 14, 1966, two days after his Gemini 11 spacecraft had been injected into orbit, Astronaut Richard F. Gordon emerged and attached to the Gemini a 100-foot line from the Agena target vehicle to which it was docked. When Gordon was back inside, "Pete" Conrad, the command pilot, undocked the Gemini from the Agena and backed away to pull the line taut. Then, firing his control jets sideways, he imparted a rotating motion of about two degrees a second, or one-third of a complete revolution per minute, to the orbiting "dumbbell."

This slow-rotating movement created a slight centrifugal force, equivalent to a gravity pull of about 1/1,000 of a G, that shoved the astronauts very gently back into their seats. For the first time, even though on a modest scale, artificial gravity had been created in a manned spacecraft.

The feat had taken tricky maneuvering. As the two-inch-wide tether line was being pulled from its storage bag on the Agena, the resulting tugs on that craft repeatedly made it yaw around. Finally, the Gemini drew the tether taut, but it took quite a while for the Agena to stop its oscillations and line up steadily with the tether. Even after a spin was imparted to the dumbbell configuration, the centrifugal acceleration did not steady down to a constant value at once because the elastic Dacron-webbing tether line behaved like a spring and kept on contracting and expanding for a long time.

Conrad and Gordon completed about 2½ orbits around the

earth in the slowly revolving configuration. They proved that two spacecraft in orbit can be tied together with a long rope—and that a slow rotation can effectively prevent the two craft from getting tangled up or colliding with each other. This means that extended formation flying in orbit will be possible, henceforth, without a prohibitive expenditure of propellants for "station-keeping."

The experiment proved, too, that the low centrifugal force resulting from the spin is acceptable and does not result in discomfort for the crew.

In this pioneering trial, however, the spin was too slow and the centrifugal acceleration too weak to answer these long-asked questions:

Is spin-induced centrifugal force an adequate substitute for the missing gravitational force in unpowered orbital flight? And, indeed, is artificial gravity desirable at all?

Early concepts of manned space stations provided for spin-induced artificial gravity because of the complete lack of knowledge as to whether a human being could stand prolonged weightlessness. Flights through "ballistic trajectories" in rocket- and jet-powered aircraft could simulate this eerie condition for a minute or two. But without actual manned flights into orbit it was impossible to find out whether zero gravity was acceptable for days, weeks, or months.

We know today, after Frank Borman's and James Lovell's fourteen-day flight in Gemini 7, that two weeks of zero gravity is not hazardous and does not impair pilots' proficiency. But we still cannot say whether zero gravity would be acceptable for permanent space stations or for interplanetary voyages lasting for months. It is indeed likely that spin-induced artificial gravity will be used for such projects.

Considerations favoring artificial gravity are partly medical, partly practical. Let us look first at the medical aspects:

Among the most fabulous sensing devices in the human body are the "vestibular organs" of the inner ear. They consist of two major subsystems: The "semicircular canals" are filled with a liquid; as you nod your head up or down the tiny pressure difference between the ends of the canal generates a signal to the brain that indicates *angular acceleration*. The "otolith apparatus" is a pebble-sized bone embedded in a jellylike substance and floating on hairs. The hairs project out of sensory cells and the signal of those hairs that report the greatest load from the otolith is accepted by the brain as the "down" direction. The otolith apparatus responds to *linear accelerations*.

The vestibular organs, we know, can be easily upset. Some people get dizzy on a merry-go-round. Some are subject to seasickness. Vertigo can play tricks even on experienced jet pilots.

Moreover, the effect of sudden zero gravity is known to throw the body into a state of alert. In everyday life zero gravity means free fall—caused voluntarily if we jump from a diving board or involuntarily if we fall from a ladder. In either case a potentially dangerous impact is imminent, and the body is alerted to brace itself for it by the otolith's zero-gravity message to the brain.

What if there were no impact and no "all clear" signal either after the otolith flashed its zero-gravity alarm signal to the brain? Some medical men feared dire effects on the proficiency of astronauts prior to man's first ventures into outer space. We know now that this problem does not exist—at least, not for experienced pilots who have been through many limited periods of zero-G. In fact, all our astronauts have commented that if zero gravity posed a problem at all, it was the feeling of extreme comfort—which tended to induce sleep and made it a little harder to stay wide awake during periods of little activity or excitement. Possibly the greatest readjustment problem was getting used to normal gravity again, particularly after splashing down in the ocean and being tossed about by the waves.

Medical studies indicate that prolonged zero gravity does have some physical effects quite similar to those of extended rest in bed. For example, the body's lower extremities act as a pool in which much of our blood supply is kept by gravity when we are standing upright, but they do not do so either in bed rest or in zero gravity. On the average, therefore, the heart has to pump more fluid daily when we are lying in bed or are in zero gravity.

As a result, the heart flashes a signal to the kidneys to extract some of the blood's water, which is excreted as urine within a day or two. At the end of the bed rest or exposure to zero gravity in space flight the blood volume is promptly restored by an urge to drink water.

Practical considerations may offer more reason for introducing artificial gravity in space stations and interplanetary spacecraft. When dirt doesn't fall to the floor, but keeps floating in mid-air, it can get awfully messy after a while. A spacecraft cabin may be spic-and-span and surgically clean at takeoff; but after several weeks of eating, drinking, conducting scientific experiments, and unpacking and storing auxiliary equipment—not to speak of the functions of body hygiene—things can become pretty clammy. Under artificial gravity you can fry an egg in a pan, lay a book on a table, vacuum the floor, take a shower, and lead a normal life.

Even more important, you can use research equipment designed for normal earth laboratories under artificial gravity. You don't have to redesign basic gear to make it compatible with the zero-G environment of a space laboratory.

The first scientists have already joined our astronaut program, but today the demands on physical qualifications are still high. Astronautics is still in the experimental stage, and any astronaut should be capable of withstanding the physical strains of sudden emergencies.

Likewise, a decade ago, jet aircraft were something for professional pilots to worry about. The field has now been invaded by grandfathers, elderly ladies, and babies, while parachute storage space has been replaced by television, stereo music, and fancy food service.

A decade from now most of the inhabitants of a space station will be astronomers, bio-scientists, medical researchers, engineers, and meteorologists. Today's astronaut will have moved up into the role of a station commander or member of his staff. And as space activities come to include more people from normal walks of life, artificial gravity will be the popular thing to have—because it makes life in space more like life at home.

Rendezvous in Space

When a spacecraft's pilot altered its orbit, in the Gemini 3 flight of Virgil I. Grissom and John W. Young in March, 1965, the feat was hailed as historic. For the first time a manned spacecraft was maneuvered from one orbit to another. In this case there were three successive changes, both in the height and in the inclination of the orbit.

The feat was important because it was the first successful trial of a system designed to maneuver a manned spacecraft for rendezvous and docking. And the capability of two space vehicles to meet, and latch on to each other, was a key requirement for many subsequent Gemini space flight objectives and also for the Apollo lunar landing program.

For example, Apollo's Lunar Module, bearing two astronauts returning from the lunar surface, must rendezvous and then dock with the Service and Command Module. The latter, with its lonely "shipkeeper," will have been orbiting around the moon during the LM's descent to the lunar surface and its re-ascent. Rendezvous is the only way to get all three Apollo astronauts back to earth. (*See* Chapter 23 "Beating the Perils of Manned Space Flight.")

Space stations, repair missions, space refueling, and satellite inspection all require a well-developed technique of orbital rendezvous and docking.

Gemini 3, the first manned Gemini flight, attempted just that. Gemini 6, with Astronaut Walter M. Schirra as command pilot and Thomas P. Stafford as pilot, succeeded in carrying out the world's first rendezvous maneuver when, on December 16, 1965, it pulled alongside Gemini 7. This spacecraft, with Frank Borman and James Lovell on board, had been launched on December 4th and returned to earth only on December 18th after completing the longest manned spaced flight ever—a full two weeks.

In March, 1966, Astronauts Armstrong and Scott conducted the world's first docking maneuver when they latched their Gemini 8 spacecraft on to a previously launched Agena rocket with which they had successfully rendezvoused. In the subsequent flights of Gemini 9, 10, and 11 this feat was repeated three times without a hitch. The problem of rendezvous and docking can therefore be considered as solved.

Out of a number of possible rendezvous flight profiles, the so-called concentric-orbit method had been chosen for all Gemini/Agena rendezvous exercises. Here is an example of the resulting flightplan:

An unmanned Atlas/Agena D target vehicle and the two-man Titan II/Gemini spacecraft have a simultaneous countdown at Cape Kennedy.

The target vehicle is launched first. After Atlas burnout, the

Agena D is fired up and injected into a circular orbit 160 miles high, inclined 28.87 degrees to the plane of the equator.

About 100 minutes later, on the first orbital pass of the Agena over the Cape area, the two-stage Titan II launch vehicle injects the Gemini spacecraft into an elliptical orbit inside the Agena's circular one. This elliptical orbit has a perigee, or lowest altitude, of 87 miles; and an apogee, or highest altitude, of 140 miles. (All distances, thus far and subsequently, are in nautical miles; the corresponding figures in ordinary statute miles would be about fifteen percent larger.)

It is very important that the Agena's and Gemini's orbits be nearly "co-planar"—in the same plane, like two figures drawn on the same sheet of paper. The permissible inclination between the two orbital planes is approximately half a degree.

To attain such accuracy is quite a trick. During the 100 minutes that elapse between the launches of target vehicle and spacecraft, the earth's spinning will turn the Cape Kennedy launch site twenty-five degrees toward the east—while the Agena's orbit remains fixed in space. This problem of the earth's rotation can be minimized by selecting an orbital plane whose northernmost point nearly coincides with the latitude of the Cape. Nevertheless, it is still necessary to actively steer and change the azimuth heading of the Titan II booster during its powered-flight phase to make the planes of the two orbits coincide.

The period of revolution of the Gemini spacecraft around the earth, along its inner elliptical orbit, is about 1½ minutes shorter than that of the Agena target. This difference gives the Gemini—the "chaser" vehicle—a 5½-degree-per-orbit "catch-up" rate on the target.

The spacecraft's launching is so timed that the Gemini will be about twenty miles behind and twenty miles below the Agena after 3½ orbits (when it has swung out to its apogee for the third time, about six hours after launch). In this relative position the Gemini now turns on its spacecraft propulsion and "circularizes" its hitherto elliptical orbit, at 140-mile altitude.

The Gemini astronauts start their actual closing-in maneuver from this circular 140-mile-high orbit. The Agena target vehicle is space-stabilized by an attitude-control system employing gyroscopes and little thrusters. It displays a flashing light, easily de-

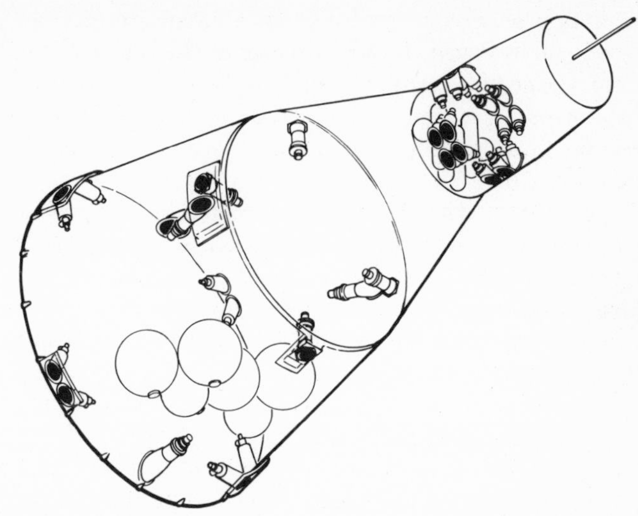

To change orbits, Gemini uses 16 small thrusters (black dots show nozzles) on the wide part of the craft. Others, on the narrow nose, aid in re-entry.

tected against the star background.

The Gemini's pilot has two control sticks, one in each hand. They activate little thrusters—midget rocket engines of 25 to 100 pounds' thrust apiece. In airless space, these provide the vital control forces that an airplane gets by deflecting its aerodynamic control surfaces.

By moving one of the sticks, the Gemini pilot can point the nose of the spacecraft up or down, and turn it left or right. With the other stick he can move the entire craft up or down, shift it sideways, or push it forward or backward.

Using this manual control, the Gemini pilot brings his spacecraft closer to the target, which all the time is flashing its light in the sky ahead of him and above him. By preventing the flashing light from drifting up, down, or sideways, with respect to the star field, he keeps his own craft on a "collision" course with the target.

The Gemini's on-board radar keeps him informed of the remaining distance to the Agena, and the closing rate (relative approach speed). As the distance diminishes, the Gemini's excess speed is reduced.

About twenty minutes or so after initiation of the closing-in maneuver, the two vehicles will be within a quarter of a mile of each other, and the relative velocity will have been reduced to eight or ten feet a second (about 5½ to seven m.p.h.). From this position the final docking phase begins.

Windows in the spacecraft provide ample vision to perform the docking manually. The Agena target vehicle is equipped with a "docking collar" designed to absorb shock loads produced by a collision velocity up to 1½ feet a second (about one m.p.h.). The docking mechanism includes a latch that prevents the Gemini spacecraft, on making contact with the target Agena, from breaking loose again.

Once the two vehicles are coupled, the pilot of the Gemini can maneuver the combination as if it were a single spacecraft.

To conclude their mission, the Gemini astronauts uncouple their spacecraft from the target Agena. Then, using its thrusters, the Gemini spacecraft backs away—and returns to earth by itself.

Guiding Spacecraft to Other Worlds

Spacecraft aimed at the moon or a planet are sometimes launched directly into their deep-space trajectory. In the more recent past, however, they were first placed into a so-called parking orbit around the earth. After one or several revolutions the uppermost stage of the launch rocket was then restarted to drive the spacecraft on to its destination. What advantage is offered by a parking orbit? From the point of view of celestial mechanics, a rocket could be launched from any point on earth *directly* to the moon or any planet. Placing the rocket temporarily in a parking orbit (around the earth) first is solely for convenience in carrying out the operation. It greatly widens the "launch window," the time span during which the launch may be executed.

Take a launching from Cape Kennedy to the moon. The Cape whirls around the earth's axis once in twenty-four hours, while the moon orbits the earth about once a month. Hence, the task of hitting the moon can be compared with that of shooting a running rabbit from a revolving merry-go-round. Your "firing window" is short—you can fire only during the brief interval when the rabbit is in sight. Next time around your aim must change, because the rabbit has moved on.

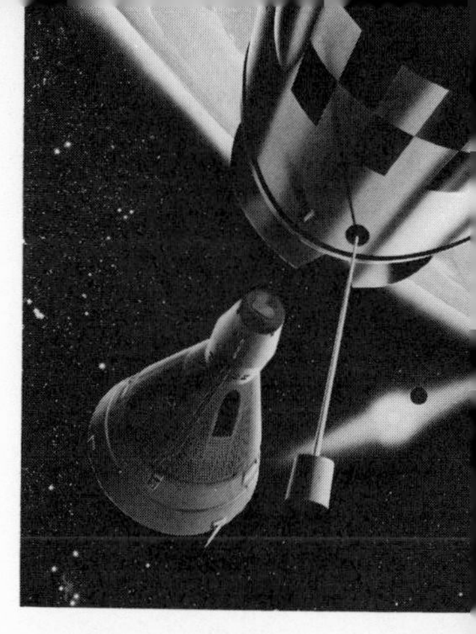

Now, it is still a rather tricky business to get a complex multi-stage rocket off its launch pad at precisely the right instant. It would be very awkward indeed if the whole complicated set of earth-to-moon guidance instructions had to be changed just because the zero time was missed by only a few seconds.

From the vantage point of the lunar target, however, it can be seen that there is only one point of the trajectory at which precise timing is really critical. That is where the rocket enters its long, unpowered "transfer" path to the moon, the so-called "translunar injection point."

Gemini spacecraft maneuvers to approach Agena target vehicle, then latches on to it.

A parking orbit divides the earth-to-moon journey into two distinctly separate phases of powered flight: the launch-to-orbit portion and the orbit-to-lunar-injection part. The rocket's "stay time" in the parking orbit, until the right moment comes to start it on the second phase of its flight to the moon, may be a few minutes or several hours.

Thus a parking orbit provides desirable slack between the "flexible" or possibly unpredictable timing of the ground launching and the "frozen" timing for translunar injection.

On the way to the moon or a distant planet a rocket's aim is refined by a mid-course correction maneuver. This is a powered maneuver to correct any inaccuracies of its "injection" into its trajectory—the start it has been given by its launch rocket.

The term "mid-course" does not necessarily mean that this maneuver will be conducted at the halfway point to a celestial target. For propellant economy, it is advantageous to perform the mid-course correction maneuver well ahead of the midway point—in fact, the sooner the better. However, to give the correct flight path the highest possible accuracy, it is necessary to wait long enough to track precisely and nail down the original uncorrected trajectory.

There may be just one mid-course correction maneuver—or several successive ones. One correction usually will suffice if accuracy requirements for the spacecraft's approach to its target are not too stringent. Missions involving extreme precision, such as orbital capture by the moon or a planet or pinpoint landings on a preselected spot on the moon, are likely to require two or more corrections.

NASA's spectacularly successful Mariner II Venus probe provides a fine example of this correctional maneuver:

Mariner II, a product of NASA's famed Jet Propulsion Laboratory, was launched on August 27, 1962, from Cape Canaveral (now Cape Kennedy). A converted Atlas D intercontinental rocket was the launch vehicle, and an Agena B served as second stage.

The Agena's rocket engine was shut down after Mariner II's successful injection into a parking orbit, 115 miles up. After a thirteen-minute coast along this orbit, the engine was restarted. It kept firing until the Agena B, with the 447-pound Mariner II spacecraft still strapped to its nose, was injected into an escape trajectory toward Venus at 25,700 m.p.h. This occurred approximately over Ascension Island in the South Atlantic Ocean, about twenty-five minutes after launch.

About two minutes later, Mariner II was separated from the burned-out Agena; its aerodynamic shroud had already been jettisoned at Atlas burnout five minutes after lift-off.

About an hour after launch, Mariner II was instructed, by radio command from the ground, to "acquire the sun." The spacecraft was equipped with six sun sensors (light-sensitive diodes) that provided a complete field of view, covering all directions. The sun, by far the sky's brightest object, could be mistaken for nothing else. The sensors, wired to the valves of a nitrogen-jet attitude control system, turned the spacecraft until its long axis pointed at the sun.

Mariner II's butterfly panels with their 9,000 solar cells, unfolded by a previous radio command, were thus swung into position to be bathed in continuous sunlight. No longer did the instruments depend on feeble chemical batteries.

One week after launch, Mariner II was instructed to aim its directional dish antenna toward the earth. During this "earth acquisition," the spacecraft maintained its lock on the sun. But it rolled on its long axis (pointed at the sun) in response to a short blast from the gas nozzles—and, with its dish antenna tilted at a preset angle, started "looking" for the earth.

Successful acquisition of the earth by the large directional antenna manifested itself by a sharp rise in signal strength. (Up to that moment, all communications had been through a separate, nondirectional spacecraft antenna.) In this position, a small counterblast of the gas nozzles stopped the spacecraft's roll.

Mariner II now coasted along its unpowered trajectory toward Venus, stabilized on two axes—its long axis pointing at the sun, its directional antenna at the earth. In this attitude it began its midcourse correction maneuver—which was carried out, eight days after launch, on September 4, 1962.

Up to this time, tracking data collected by three eighty-five-foot radars—spaced far apart in California, South Africa, and Australia, for continuous coverage from the rotating earth—had been fed into an electronic computer. The computer compared the actual trajectory of Mariner II with the trajectory required to pass Venus at a distance of about 10,000 miles. Thus it provided data

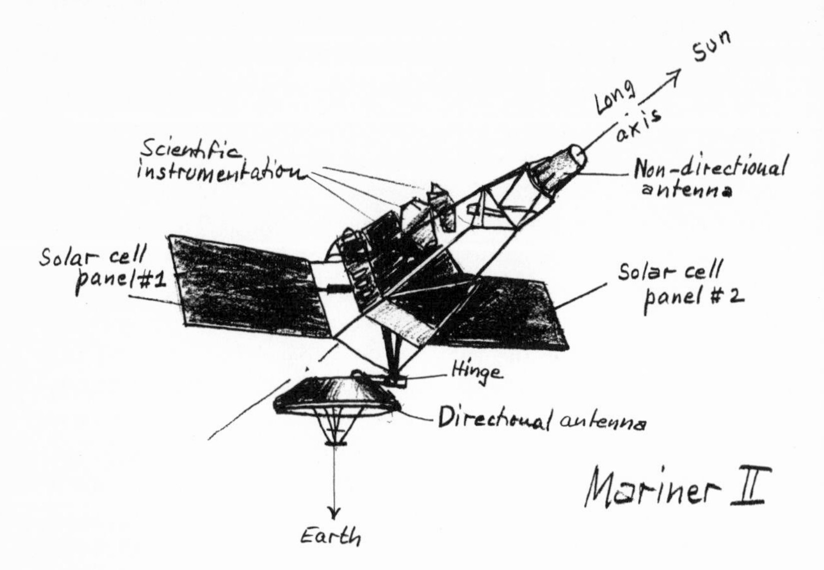

for correcting the actual trajectory, to offset its deviations from the desired one.

These data now were radioed to the spacecraft, in three distinct commands:

1. Roll through a certain angle about the spacecraft-sun axis.
2. Pitch up through a certain angle. (That is, turn the outer end of one of the two butterfly panels a bit more toward the sun, and the opposite panel's outer end away from the sun.)
3. Fire a little 50-pound-thrust motor until a certain velocity has been added in the direction of Mariner II's long axis. (The rocket motor could contribute up to 200 feet per second.)

With these three commands properly executed, Mariner II was "in the groove." To get its temperature control and communications system back in good shape, the spacecraft reacquired sun and earth. It remained in this attitude during the rest of its journey and its approach to Venus, when it activated its data-gathering instruments.

After a 180-million-mile flight, Mariner II passed Venus on December 14, 1962, at a distance of 21,000 miles. It radioed back invaluable and unprecedented data, and lifted the first veils from the mysteries of this intriguing planet.

How We Track Our Spacecraft

A few minutes after a group of spectators see a space vehicle blast off from its launch pad at Cape Kennedy, Florida, the public-address system announces that the spacecraft has been successfully injected into an orbit with a period of revolution of 88.6 minutes, a perigee altitude of 99.6 nautical miles, an apogee altitude of 122 nautical miles, and an orbital plane inclined by 31.73 degrees to the plane of the equator.

A few hours later this announcement is followed by the most detailed information on stage separation, angle-of-attack encountered in flight through layers of high wind speeds, irregularities in tank pressurization or control voltages, turbopump speeds, structural vibrations, deployment of spacecraft antennas, and many other items of information.

The tracking and data-acquisition system serving "ETR," the Eastern Test Range, makes this miracle possible. It is probably even more complex than the space vehicle whose performance was just announced. It employs optical, radar, and radio gear to look at, and listen to, the rapidly escaping bird. It involves stations on the American continent, on downrange islands, in aircraft, and aboard ships. It provides radio and cable communication links between all these stations. And it includes a set of timing signals to put all stations on a standard "time base," which is absolutely essential for meaningful data reduction.

The Eastern Test Range is served by twelve tracking stations. Range Station No. 1, by far the most elaborate, is located at and near Cape Kennedy proper. It is equipped with about everything that has ever been invented and used in this field.

A particularly important part at the Cape is played by optical equipment because, contrary to the situation at downrange stations, the bird is relatively near. Optical coverage of a launch includes:

An array of documentary cameras. Their films and still pictures not only serve for formal reporting and public information, but also have played a vital role in analyzing causes of mishaps before or shortly after launch.

Ballistic cameras, such as the Wild BC-4—an extremely precise still camera using a large, optically flat photographic plate. Several such cameras look at the bird's expected track of ascent from different vantage points. Their shutters are repeatedly opened and closed, simultaneously, by signals from the standard range timing circuit. On each plate the bright trail of a rising rocket appears as a string of beads, whose spacing grows as the rocket gathers speed. By placing the plates in a specially designed viewing machine, which works on the stereo principle, it is possible to reconstruct the trajectory with very high precision. Ballistic cameras, incidentally, are used at the down-range island stations also.

Cine-theodolites, such as the Askania Kth 53, a film camera operated by two men simultaneously. One mans the azimuth wheel; the other handles elevation. Both try to keep the bird in the cross hairs of their fields of view. Each film frame photographs the pointing direction of the camera (as indicated on the setting circles in azimuth and elevation) as well as the bird. This makes it easy to compensate for inaccurate alignment and jitter. By placing one frame of the film at a time in a compensator, which permits shifting the image of the rocket back to the picture's center, azimuth and elevation angles are corrected.

Tracking telescopes, such as the American Optical Company's Igor (Intercept Ground Optical Recorder), pictured in the photograph here. In essence this is a very powerful telescope on a mount somewhat like that of an Askania cine-theodolite, but much larger. It can produce high-resolution pictures of far-away events such as

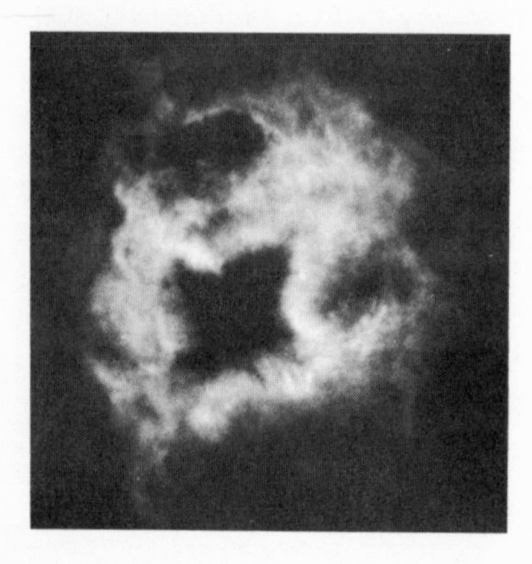

A sample photo made with the far-seeing "Igor" telescope of a striking scientific experiment at 65-mile altitude—a cloud of ice crystals that formed when a Saturn I rocket loosed 95 tons of water into the upper atmosphere.

the separation of the first rocket stage and the ignition of the second stage.

Before we come to electronic tracking equipment, let us take a quick look at the Eastern Test Range's eleven *downrange* stations. Remember, Cape Kennedy proper is Range Station No. 1 and makes up for a total of twelve tracking sites. About 100 miles to the south, still on the Florida mainland, is Station No. 2 at Jupiter Inlet. Stations 3 through 9 are respectively at Grand Bahama Island, Eleuthera Island, San Salvador, Mayaguana, Grand Turk, the Dominican Republic, and Puerto Rico. Station No. 10, at St. Lucia, has become inactive. Station No. 11 is on Fernando de Noronha, a Brazilian island. And the last of the dozen is on lonely Ascension Island, a British island eight degrees south of the equator and more than 5,000 miles from Cape Kennedy.

The Eastern Test Range's electronic tracking systems can be roughly divided into "pulse radar" and "continuous wave" equipment.

Two men at hand wheels operate "Igor," the tracking telescope, to make long-range photos of the behavior of an ascending rocket vehicle.

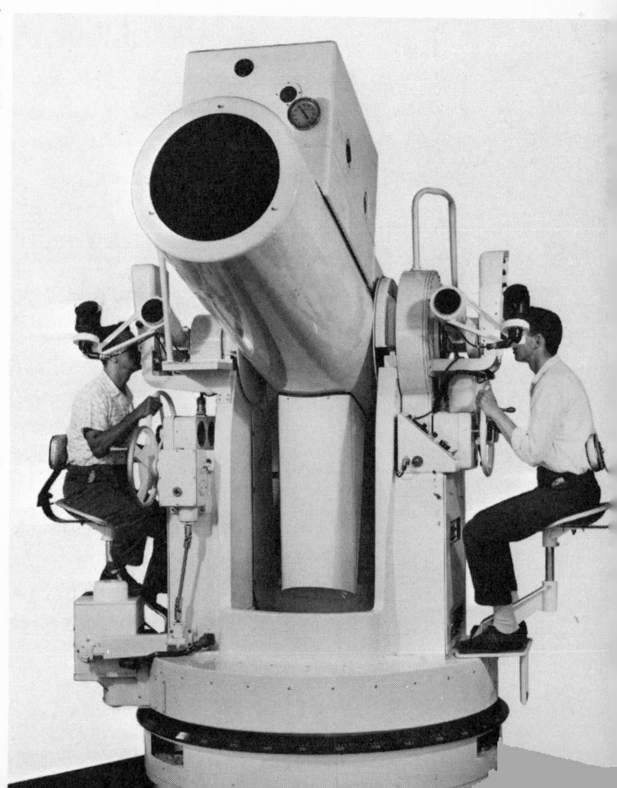

The tracking ship *General Hoyt S. Vandenberg,* seen here in an Air Force photo, is part of a fleet supplementing mainland and island stations of the Eastern Test Range.

Radar tracking is done by aiming a rapid fire of powerful radio pulses at the speeding rocket. The signals are reflected either by the rocket's metal skin ("skin tracking") or by an amplifier beacon carried in the rocket ("beacon tracking"). The same antenna dish that bundles the outgoing pulse, and aims it at the rocket, collects the returning electronic "echo" and sends it to a receiver. The slant distance from radar unit to space vehicle is shown by the elapsed time between a pulse's departure and return; the line of sight to the bird by the direction from which the loudest echo comes. The Eastern Test Range has a vast array of radar sets, ranging from venerable AN-FPS-16 units to the still-experimental AN-FPS-43. Not all of ETR's radars are used for tracking rockets, however; some (such as AN-FPS-8 units) keep the skies under surveillance for intruding aircraft or aid the tracking radars in target acquisition.

Continuous-wave tracking systems are based on the Doppler effect—the familiar phenomenon of a train whistle's drop in pitch as the locomotive passes. A continuous signal of well-stabilized frequency is sent up to the rocket. The speeding rocket receives the electromagnetic waves at a somewhat lower frequency, just like a ship running with the waves. As the received signal is radioed back to the ground station, an additional Doppler shift in the frequency occurs.

By comparing the outgoing frequency and the returning one, the ground station can thus determine precisely at what rate of speed the rocket is receding from the station, along the line of sight. By taking this measurement from several locations on the ground, simultaneously, the rocket's flight path can be determined.

Instead of several independent ground stations, however, all continuous-wave tracking systems are using one central transmitter-receiver-evaluator complex, connected to an array of rather widely dispersed antennas that are laid on the ground in a suitable geometric pattern. The system then utilizes the small differences between transmitted and received signals, as noted at the various antenna locations, to learn the space vehicle's flight path.

The Eastern Test Range has the following types of continuous-wave tracking systems: Azusa, Mistram, Udop, Odop, and Glotrac. All use the Doppler effect; their differences lie in how they utilize the effect for the highest accuracy in the determination of the flight-path.

Orbital flights launched from Cape Kennedy invariably pass over wide stretches of ocean. To assure uninterrupted tracking for critical flight phases—such as powered ascent or power maneuvers in orbit—the Eastern Test Range operates several tracking ships. Like the land-based stations of the Range, these vessels are equipped with just about everything that can nail down the exact flight path of a space vehicle.

Range ships thus become a vital factor in making space operations effective and safe. In addition to radars and computers, the ships are equipped with an inertial-guidance system similar to those used in nuclear submarines. This unit not only determines the exact location of the ship, regardless of visibility of landmarks or stars, but it also gives a reference for all radar antennas aboard and furnishes an input on pitch, yaw, and roll motions of the ship during tracking operations. During data reduction, the ship's motions are subtracted from the antenna pointings—with the result that data are, for all practical purposes, received by an antenna on a stable platform.

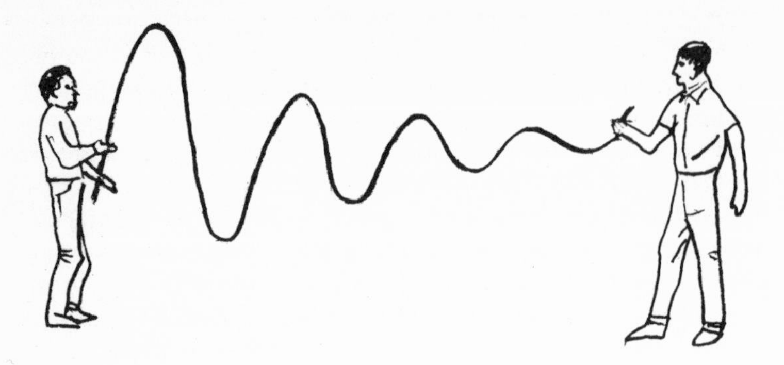

How Spacemen Use Laser Beams

The word *LASER* is an abbreviation for *L*ight *A*mplification by *S*timulated *E*mission of *R*adiation. In one form of laser, its key element is a synthetic ruby crystal, which performs the incredible feat of making all the light waves that emerge from it "march in step." Such "coherent" light can be bundled into a beam much narrower than that of the best searchlights.

Since light beams can be used just like radio waves to carry a voice, a command, or any other form of communication, a needle-sharp laser beam offers revolutionary advances in low-power communications across extremely large distances in space.

In the ruby crystal of the laser, impinging light energy from a lamp or other source can be stored temporarily, by kicking orbital electrons of some of the crystal's atoms into higher orbits of temporary but limited stability. When the first electron thus "elevated" drops back into its original lower orbit, it emits a tiny package of light called a photon. A photon may be envisioned as a rapidly attenuated light wave, comparable to a wave tossed into a rope, as in my sketch.

To understand this strange phenomenon better, consider the structure of an atom—any atom. In the simplest, the hydrogen atom, a single proton forms the nucleus and a single electron revolves around it. The nucleus of the oxygen atom consists of an array of eight protons and eight neutrons, around which revolve eight electrons in two distinct orbits. A chromium atom, found in a ruby crystal, has an even heavier nucleus with twenty-four orbiting electrons.

As an orbital electron absorbs the energy of an impinging photon, it will jump into a higher orbit whose energy level exceeds that of the original orbit by exactly the amount of energy that was brought in by the absorbed photon. The photon's energy, in turn, depends solely on the wave length of the incoming light. However, in the atom of any given element, only certain specific transitions between orbits are "permissible," while all others are "prohibited."

Therefore, the atoms of any particular element can absorb only photons of wave lengths that happen to be compatible with its own permissible set of electron orbits. When an "excited" electron—one that has been kicked into a higher orbit—falls back into the more-stable lower orbit, it emits a photon of precisely the same wave length. (The fact that elements can emit only light of certain wave lengths becomes obvious when we look at the band spectrum emitted, for example, by a glowing neon tube.)

A ruby crystal is made up of chromium, aluminum, and oxygen atoms. Certain higher "excitation" orbits in the chromium atoms are "metastable," which means the electrons can stay quite a while in the higher orbits before they drop back. Thus the crystal does not necessarily release photons at the same rate at which they are absorbed.

The ruby crystal can therefore be "pumped up" with quite a bit of light energy. However, once the first excited electron does drop back into the lower orbit—and emits its typical ruby-red light photon—the event virtually reverberates throughout the entire crystal. Every other excited electron likewise drops back and emits its photon.

The remarkable thing now is that as the ruby dumps the stored energy, the light waves of all these emitted photons are precisely "in phase"; that is, the light emitted is "coherent."

Due to the physical size of the ruby crystal (which of course is many times larger than the wave length of the emitted light), the emerging light waves do not arrive simultaneously at whatever target they hit. The situation can be best compared with a company of soldiers marching past a parade stand. While the first column passes the grandstand earlier than the last column, all the soldiers are marching in step.

A laser beam can be bundled better than ordinary light, for the narrowness of the laser beam is a direct consequence of the crystal

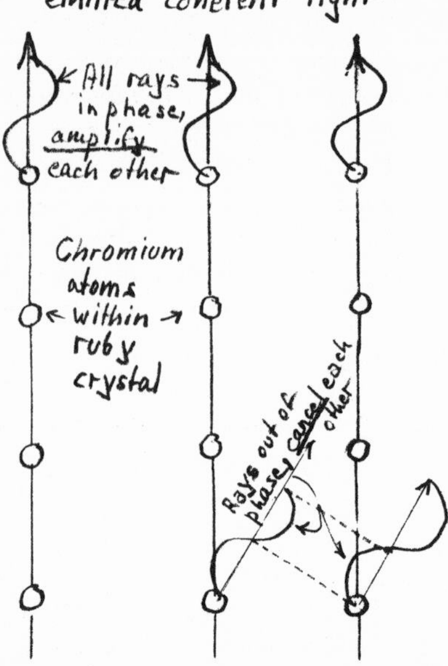

structure of the ruby. The bulk of the coherent light emitted (when the ruby dumps its stored energy) is beamed in the direction in which the chromium atoms are aligned within the crystal. This is simply due to the fact that, just as with monochromatic light passing through a grating, "interference" effects cancel much of the light emitted in other directions. (See my sketch.) Narrowing down the laser beam is limited chiefly by the accuracy to which the ruby's exit plane can be manufactured. In practice, laser beams can be made about twenty to thirty times as sharp as the best searchlight beams.

In a laser communications system, which carries a voice or a signal, the ruby is irradiated with a suitable, continuous light source, and the crystal dumps its bursts into the needle-sharp beam at the rate of many thousand times per second. The distant receiver (at which the beam, of course, must be aimed with great precision) thus seems to see a practically continuous source of red ruby light.

To carry a voice, a suitable light filter is inserted into the beam. Its filtering effect is modulated, or varied, with the electric current from a telephone mike. At the receiving end, the varying intensity of the impinging light beam is used to produce the current that drives the loudspeaker.

It has been suggested that the laser principle could also be used to generate "death rays" capable of killing soldiers at a distance of several miles or of destroying missiles or airplanes in the sky.

Any such use of the laser principle, of course, would call for a laser that could produce tremendous power surges of the order of thousands or even millions of kilowatts. In a ruby crystal the bulk of the absorbed energy is converted into useless heat, and only a small percentage is utilized for the production of the beamed surges of coherent light. As long as we are dealing with the relatively low power levels required for communications, the resulting cooling problems can be mastered. However, if we try to produce surges capable of destroying an airplane miles away, the much greater heat development within the laser system itself is liable to destroy the crystal.

Nevertheless, there is much research going on in this field, and many people believe that certain types of lasers, particularly "gas lasers" which do not use crystals, have great potential as future weapons.

Space Power from Fuel Cells

A fuel cell is an exciting new device capable of converting fuel and oxygen directly into electricity. Its efficiency is easily twice as high as that of conventional power sources. Like so many revolutionary technical concepts, the fuel cell is the direct result of the extraordinary demands of the space age.

The most advanced fuel cell uses hydrogen and oxygen, both in gaseous form. What it does amounts to the reverse of the familiar schoolroom demonstration of electrolysis. In that experiment, sending a direct current through water breaks up the water molecules, with the hydrogen gas bubbling up at one electrode and oxygen gas at the other. In the fuel cell, just the opposite happens: Hydrogen gas and oxygen gas are fed in, and out comes an electric current—and a little water.

Because of their light weight, fuel cells offer an almost ideal source of power for space vehicles. General Electric fuel cells provide electric power for the two-man Gemini spacecraft, while Pratt & Whitney fuel cells are used in the follow-on Apollo spacecraft designed to land Americans on the moon.

In our space program the use of fuel cells is firmly established, not only in spacecraft but likewise in future space stations and even on the moon's surface.

One of the most important aspects of the fuel cell—the hydrogen-oxygen fuel cell, in particular—is its by-product, water. The water from a fuel cell is potable. You can drink it as it comes out of the cell stack—and astronauts need about 6.6 pounds of water a day for life support. Also, with the help of electricity and electrolysis, water can be turned back into its two constituents, hydrogen and oxygen.

Suppose we power a vehicle roving the surface of the moon with fuel cells. Let us further suppose it is equipped with hydrogen and oxygen tanks for a radius of action of a few hundred miles. When the vehicle comes back to camp, its hydrogen and oxygen tanks may be nearly empty, but its water-collection tank, in return, will be almost full.

To "fill 'er up," the vehicle will pull into a lunar service station. This station need not be supplied with fresh hydrogen and oxygen flown in from earth. Instead, it has a large array of solar cells that convert energy from the sun into electricity. The driver of the lunar vehicle turns in his water, and his tanks are replenished with fresh hydrogen and oxygen generated in a high-pressure electrolysis plant. This plant's supply of water can, of course, be augmented by refuse water accumulated at a nearby lunar base.

It takes twenty-five square yards of solar cells to collect one horsepower from the sun. Thus, it would be awkward, if not impossible, to operate a bouncing cross-country moon rover directly with solar power. But there is nothing wrong with large solar-cell areas at the filling station to "reprocess" turned-in water in a round-the-clock operation.

The fuel cell as a source of power for lunar-surface vehicles thus becomes a convenient energy-storage device, operating a bit like a car battery. The important difference is that for the same amount of stored electric energy it is much lighter.

The hydrogen-oxygen fuel cell (the easiest to explain) operates as shown in my drawing sketch, which draws upon material pub-

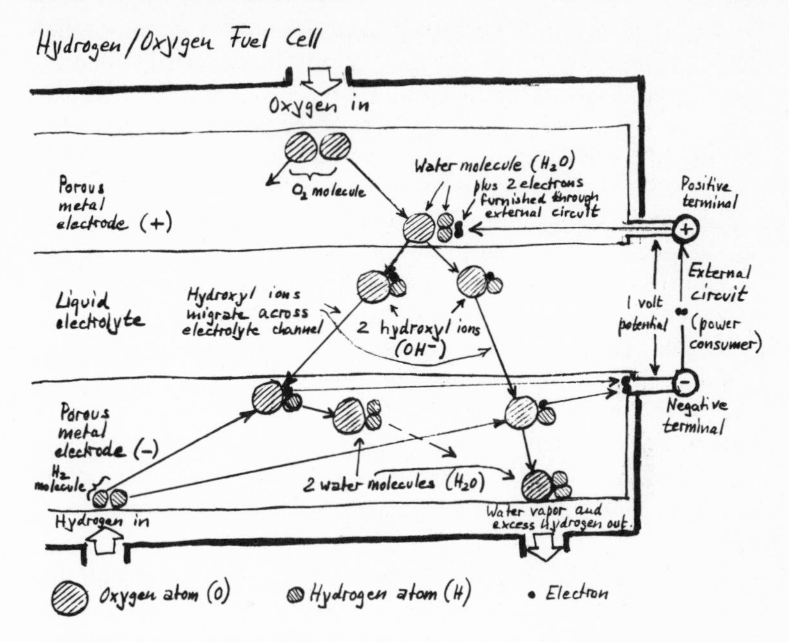

lished by Pratt & Whitney. Oxygen gas (O_2) enters at the top, and hydrogen gas (H_2) at the lower left corner. The two gases are fed into porous metal electrodes that are separated by a solution of potassium hydroxide, an "electrolyte" or electrically conductive liquid. At the electrodes occurs an important ion exchange, the key to generating electric power. The basic mechanism (as sketched) works as follows:

One oxygen atom (of the two making up an O_2 molecule), plus one water molecule (H_2O), plus two electrons, produce two hydroxyl ions (OH^-). These hydroxyl ions migrate across the electrolytic "channel." Within the porous hydrogen electrode, each hydroxyl ion latches onto one hydrogen atom (of the two making up an H_2 molecule). Two molecules of water and two free electrons are the result. The water is removed by way of an outlet at the lower right corner. The two free electrons are extracted at a terminal attached to the negative (hydrogen) electrode, which has a potential of about one volt against the positive (oxygen) electrode.

In terms of hydroelectric power this is like saying the storage lake (the negative electrode) is at a higher elevation than the drain-off river (the positive electrode). Like the water rushing through the turbines at a dam, the current of electrons produced within the negative electrode can perform useful work, in an external circuit, before reaching the lower energy level of the positive electrode. Reentering the cell there, the electrons hitchhike back through the electrolyte to their starting point on new hydroxyl ions.

One volt, of course, is not much—it is about half the voltage of a flashlight battery. But just as in a flashlight or in a car battery, we can stack cells together "in series" to multiply the voltage. My drawing sketch shows how this is done.

Despite its high efficiency, a fuel cell still generates, besides useful electricity, a certain amount of heat that must be dissipated to protect the cell. The heat is carried away by running the cell with an excess supply of hydrogen gas. This excess hydrogen also serves to drive the water generated by the fuel cell's operation to its outlet. If the water were not removed, the cell would soon "drown."

The excess hydrogen now can either be cooled in a radiator and readmitted to the cycle, or simply vented away. The choice de-

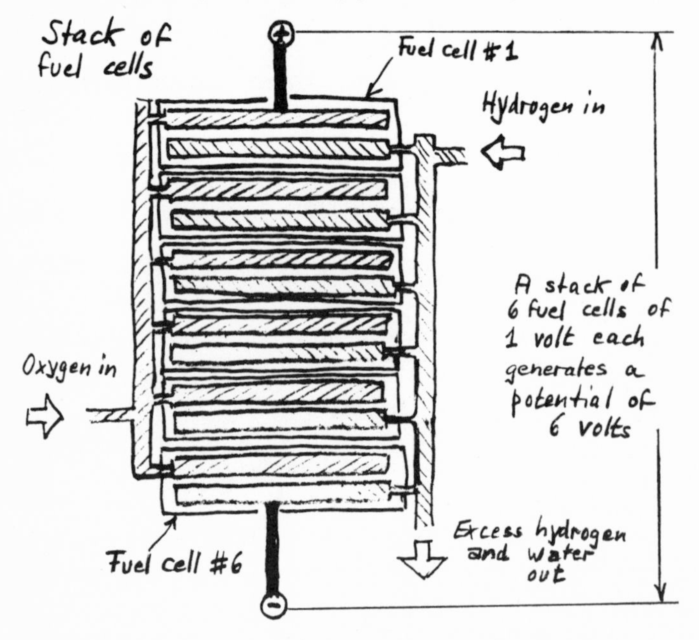

pends on a trade-off between equipment weight and propellant weight. For longer operating time, cooling and re-using the hydrogen is preferable. For shorter operation, the blow-away scheme is superior, since it does not require a cooler.

Fuel cells greatly surpass other power sources in efficiency.

Ever since the beginning of the industrial revolution, combustion of fuel has been the prime mover of all the many wheels that have started to spin. Whether in a steam or a diesel locomotive, a piston-powered automobile, or a jet-powered airplane; whether directly as in a rocket, or indirectly as in a kitchen fan (which gets its power from an electric outlet powered by a turbogenerator in a municipal utility plant)—we could always trace the source of power back to some device that burned combustible fuel, such as crude oil, natural gas, gasoline, or coal, with oxygen from the air. The fuel cell is a drastic departure from this time-honored process.

All conventional engines are restricted to what engineers call the "Carnot-cycle efficiency." Nicolas Leonard Sadi Carnot, a French scientist, showed that even under ideal conditions—the Carnot cycle—a heat engine cannot convert into mechanical energy all the heat energy supplied to it.

In a Carnot cycle, an engine accepts heat energy from a high-temperature source, such as hot steam from a boiler or the combustion of gasoline in the cylinder of a piston engine. It converts part of the energy into mechanical work—for instance, by allowing the steam or combustion gas to push against a piston or a turbine blade. But to keep the process going, the engine must reject the rest of the energy to a "heat sink" or cold body.

This is the reason that automobiles need water cooling and radiators, aircraft engines need air cooling, and steam turbines need water-cooled condensers. For Carnot showed that in order to increase the efficiency of a heat engine, it is necessary to increase the temperature *difference* between the heat *source* and the heat *sink*. Heat engines are limited to overall efficiencies of the order of thirty percent by the inherent restrictions of this Carnot cycle.

The fuel cell is not tied to this cycle. Efficiencies of sixty percent and more have been demonstrated. Hence, the great interest in this byproduct of the space age.

It is a safe bet that fuel cells will find increasing acceptance on earth as well as in space. Recently a fuel-cell-powered tractor was demonstrated. Fuel cells running on oil and natural gas, rather than hydrogen, are already being tested. While it may be premature to predict imminent doom for the conventional heat engine, many believe that the days of any engine restricted by the Carnot cycle are numbered.

Electric Power Sources in Space

Fuel cells, as described in Chapter 18, made their space debut in the third Gemini flight on March 23, 1965. A single hydrogen-oxygen fuel cell replaced some of the silver-zinc batteries that the two-man Gemini spacecraft had used before. Likewise, fuel cells will furnish electricity in the three-man Apollo spacecraft that will go to the moon.

Space vehicles need electric power, both in rocket-propelled and coasting flight, for all sorts of vital gear: life-support systems, radio, propulsion control, guidance, instruments, and more. Electric power will be required, too, for a lunar base.

Advancing technology offers a widening choice of electric-power sources for space—chemical batteries, fuel cells, solar cells, atomic batteries, and nuclear reactors, to name the more-important ones. Which of these systems will a space-vehicle designer choose, and why?

Chemical batteries have been a mainstay since the Space Age's beginning. They powered the earliest satellites—Russia's first two Sputniks and our Explorer I. All our manned spacecraft, of the Mercury and Gemini flights, have depended on them. Chemical batteries are still unchallenged as electric-power sources for launch rockets, which demand as much as several kilowatts of power, though for only a few minutes.

Advanced types like silver-zinc and nickel-cadmium batteries offer more power for less weight than the less-expensive lead battery in your car. However, chemical batteries are prohibitively heavy for long use—more than a very few weeks—without recharging.

Fuel cells, while related to chemical batteries in principle, represent quite a radical departure in form. Hydrogen gas and oxygen gas are fed into the tanklike fuel cell. What comes out is an electric current—up to a kilowatt or two, in present designs for spacecraft —and a little water.

A fuel cell thus requires a supply of hydrogen and oxygen, carried along as high-pressure gases or in liquefied form—and can operate only so long as the supply holds out.

For manned space vehicles, however, a fuel cell's attractions are enhanced by the fact that the water it produces is potable. Drinking water must be provided for the astronauts anyway. So it might as well be taken along in the form of hydrogen and oxygen—which, combining in the fuel cell, will generate electricity and replenish the drinking-water dispenser in the bargain.

Fuel cells are attractive for lunar surface vehicles, too. They would make "moon cars" independent of the sunshine required by solar cells, and free of the radiation problems of nuclear power. Water produced by a day's run on fuel cells could be turned back into hydrogen and oxygen at a stationary electrolysis plant run by solar or nuclear energy.

Solar cells, of which a bank makes up a solar battery, have a theoretically unlimited lifetime. These are small shingles of pure silicon, whose outer surfaces have been contaminated by exposure to boron vapor. Sunlight striking these cells is converted directly into current. Here is how this works:

The smallest unit to which electricity can be reduced is the *electron.* Similarly, light energy cannot be subdivided beyond a unit called a *photon.*

A light photon impinging on the boron-contaminated surface of a silicon shingle is absorbed within a layer not exceeding 1/100,000 of an inch in depth. Its absorption invariably leads to the displacement of an electron. While free electrons are few and far between within the boron-containing layer, they are in ample supply in the pure silicon beneath. As a result, when enough energy has been imparted to a displaced electron to propel it from the boron-doped layer into the pure-silicon region, it is free to move into an external circuit where it helps to deliver power.

Solar batteries produce only a few watts of electrical power per square foot of panel surface. In order to drive high-powered transmitters for deep-space communication, they usually feed their weak but round-the-clock power into a chemical storage battery capable of high-power, short-time discharges.

The Vanguard I satellite, launched in 1958, was the first to use solar battery power. It is still operating.

The output of solar-cell installations has grown from Vanguard I's tiny 0.06-watt power to 200 watts in our Mariner IV Mars spacecraft. For higher ratings, they become cumbersome, since a square foot of solar cells yields only a few watts. To avoid this drawback, makers are experimenting with flexible solar-cell "tapes" that can be wrapped around large space-vehicle structures.

Many orbiting space vehicles pass through the earth's shadow at regular intervals but need a continuous supply of power. Solar cells must then be supplemented by rechargeable chemical batteries. In sunlight, the solar cells supply power needs, and also charge the chemical batteries; in shadow, the chemical batteries temporarily carry the load.

Atomic batteries use the heat given off by the natural decay of various radioactive isotopes, such as plutonium 238, curium 244, or promethium 147. Thermocouples turn this heat into electric current.

An atomic battery called SNAP-9A provides the twenty-watt power of one Navy navigation satellite presently in orbit. SNAP stands for "Systems for Nuclear Auxiliary Power," of which a number are being developed jointly by NASA and the AEC for space use.

Such radioactive-isotope batteries can supply up to several hundred watts of electricity for periods well over a year. For needs within those figures, they have now become competitive with solar cells.

Besides heat, atomic batteries inevitably emit a certain amount of undesirable radiation, against which a space crew and radiation-sensitive equipment must be shielded. Also, there is a potential hazard, when a spacecraft breaks up during re-entry, of scattering radioactive material that will sink to earth, and may slightly raise the radiation level of a surface area. Some radioisotopes are less hazardous than others, and their use minimizes the risk.

Nuclear reactors provide power, not from radioactive isotopes that decay spontaneously at an invariable rate but from a controllable chain reaction. This requires an amount of fissionable material, such as uranium 235, exceeding a certain "critical" mass. So a nuclear reactor would not make sense where only a few watts of power is needed, but it becomes attractive once we talk about kilowatts—especially several hundred kilowatts or more.

For example, nuclear reactors will find use in future high-powered TV broadcasting satellites—which, hovering in a "synchronous" orbit, will be capable of beaming TV programs directly into your home set.

They will be used, too, in manned planetary vehicles—whose long voyages will call for more comfort, and also for more radio-transmitting power, than is needed in orbiting the earth or in going to the moon.

And, speaking of the moon, nuclear reactors undoubtedly will be used to provide electric power for future lunar-base camps.

The first nuclear reactor in space, a 230-pound one called SNAP-10A, was orbited for trial in 1965. Its flight test proved that such a power plant could be subjected to a rocket launching and then be started and operated in orbit.

In SNAP-10A thermoelectric elements turn heat from the nuclear chain reaction into electricity, and so there are no moving parts. Although SNAP-10A yields only five hundred watts, the same thermoelectric principle can be applied to produce up to about twenty kilowatts. Still higher-powered nuclear reactors for space will heat steam or another gas, such as mercury vapor, to drive a turbogenerator.

How much power is needed, and for how long, obviously will enter into a designer's choice of which space-power system to use. In addition, there is an all-important consideration:

The source of power must be extremely reliable. No single component's failure must ever be permitted to deprive a space vehicle of all its vital power. Hence, just as solar cells, atomic batteries, and fuel cells had to await thorough proof of their reliability before being adopted for use in space, so will other promising innovations in electric-power supply that are still in the experimental stage today.

Coming . . . Ferries to Space

In the not too distant future we may expect to see spacecraft put into orbit in a new way. Many of them will be borne aloft by winged and manned vehicles that resemble airplanes more than rockets—and that may even take off horizontally in airplane fashion, rather than vertically like rockets. The most important thing about these radical launch vehicles is that they will return safely to earth, to be used over and over again.

Space flight today is still awfully expensive. Among the biggest items of cost, of course, are the large launch rockets required to hurl manned and unmanned spacecraft into orbit or beyond.

Up to now all launch rockets have been strictly one-shot vehicles. Whether or not a spacecraft reaches its orbit and performs as expected, the launch vehicle is invariably consumed in the process.

Even with our most advanced launch vehicles, it still costs about five hundred dollars to send one pound of net payload into orbit. We must drastically reduce this cost if we are to take full advantage of the tremendous potentials of space flight for scientific, and military purposes as well as public services. Re-usable launch vehicles will provide a way.

I think we can expect a re-usable launch vehicle to become available at some time between 1975 and 1980. We can expect such a vehicle to be capable of at least fifty to a hundred flights to orbit. There is no reason why it could not make at least one flight weekly. Under these assumptions, we can expect the cost of orbital transportation to drop from the present five hundred dollars a pound to fifty dollars a pound, or even less.

In my judgment, for reasons that I shall come to presently, the needs of a suitable design for the first generation of a re-usable launch vehicle point toward a manned craft that will be capable of carrying something like a dozen passengers, plus about five tons of cargo, into a low earth orbit.

Envision an aircraft the size of one of our big jet airliners. This is the first stage of the re-usable launch vehicle. Nestled on its back is the second stage—a smaller aircraft shaped like the space glider of the now defunct Dyna-Soar project, or one of the "lifting-body" configurations under current study. Both first and second stages are manned—the first stage with a flight crew, the second stage with a flight crew plus passengers, if any.

The first stage may be powered either with liquid-rocket engines or with supersonic turbojet engines. If rocket engines are used, it may take off vertically like one of our present-day space boosters

—or it may be launched horizontally from a catapult. In the case of air-breathing engines, a catapult-type horizontal launch is mandatory.

A rocket-powered first stage would accelerate to about Mach 6 before letting the second stage go. After staging, it would descend into the denser atmosphere, while turning around 180 degrees and slowing down. At a proper altitude and speed a set of cruise jet engines—hitherto retracted into the body or wings—are lowered to drive the first stage back to the launch base. Meanwhile the rocket-powered second stage has gone on into orbit.

In the case of an air-breathing first stage, staging is likely to occur at a speed not exceeding Mach 3. To make orbit from this lower initial speed, the rocket-propelled second stage must carry more propellants, and thus be larger. On the other hand, the first stage can return to base with the same set of engines used for the boost phase.

For the orbiting second stage to return to the launch base, it is only necessary to wait for the earth to roll around. Just as with Mercury and Gemini flights, the retromaneuver in orbit must be initiated at a time when the launch base moves into the area where the re-entry flight path will terminate.

An "orbital transport" vehicle such as this could serve, for one example, to carry men to and from orbiting space stations and to replenish the stations' supplies—as well as to carry out a great variety of other missions in space.

There are no insurmountable difficulties in designing and developing a re-usable launch vehicle on the basis of presently available technology. We need not wait for any great breakthrough in scien-

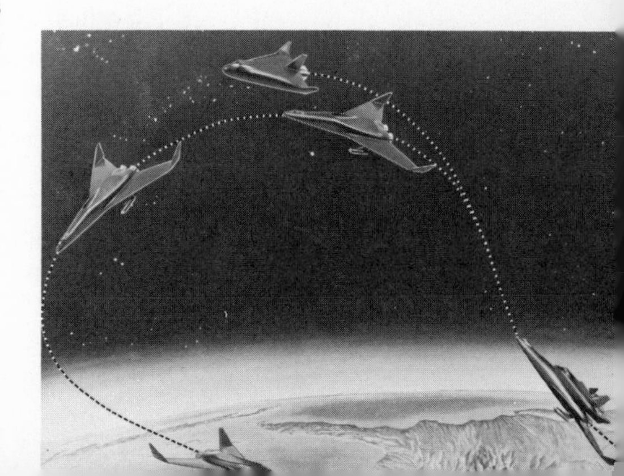

A flight plan for future launching with recoverable vehicle. A two-stage piggyback craft takes off like an airplane and zooms to high altitude and hypersonic velocity. The second stage separates and accelerates under its own rocket power to orbital speed, while the winged first stage descends and returns to base.

tific research to come up with quite an attractive design. On the other hand, if the decision to wait with the actual development of such a vehicle was postponed for a few years, advances in materials and propulsion research would undoubtedly enable us to create an even better concept. For instance, there is much promising work going on with the so-called whisker composite materials, tiny single-crystal fibers of silicon carbide or aluminum oxide embedded in aluminum or epoxy resin, which offer many times the strength of the best metals and will permit the design of much lighter structures. Also, instead of having to chose between rocket and air-breathing propulsion, it seems entirely feasible to create a propulsion system which at take-off works like a turbojet engine, then converts into a ramjet, and at near-orbital speeds operates like a pure rocket, burning its fuel in liquified air, scooped up and liquified during the earlier part of the ascent. A re-usable launch vehicle propelled by such a SCRAMLACE (Supersonic Combustion RAMjet Liquid Air Cycle Engine) would have the potential of flying to orbit without dropping off a stage, and to return to the take-off base for another flight.

If we stick to the more conventional two-stage concepts based on today's technology, things are comparable to the much-discussed "SST," the Supersonic Transport. While competitive studies, aerodynamic refinements, and engine advances will undoubtedly continue to improve the economic aspects of that future supersonic airplane, nobody doubts the basic feasibility of the project.

But in another way, there is an important difference between the two projects. A worldwide airline system, served by subsonic jets at the present time, already exists. Marketing planners for the SST know that as soon as the first airline puts a supersonic transport in operation on one of the heavily traveled long-distance routes, competition will force all other carriers flying the same route to follow suit. Thus the planners can clearly foresee, even today, the potential sales volume for the SST—and they have a fairly reliable basis for comparing development cost with expected or, at least, hoped-for sales.

Unfortunately, our crystal ball for the future sales volume of re-usable space launch vehicles is not nearly as clear.

To be sure, there is plenty of space traffic. Between January 31,

1958, and March 31, 1965, the United States launched no less that 287 rockets into space, of which 222 were successful. But the payloads of these rockets varied widely, from only a few pounds up to more than ten tons. The space routes ranged from low orbits, barely skimming the outer fringes of the earth's atmosphere, to interplantary trajectories grazing our neighbor planets.

Before we can set out to spend a billion dollars or more to develop a re-usable launch vehicle, we must seek for it a many-purpose capability that will satisfy at least a major portion of our space-transportation needs for the next decade or so.

The particular launch vehicle that I have described exemplifies such a "common" design—and the reasoning leading to it goes something like this:

Just like airliners, which make no money while sitting on the ground, re-usable launch vehicles must be kept flying—the more, the better.

Now, we have reason to believe that the greatest number of space flights—manned and unmanned—will be conducted in low orbits around the earth. They offer the best vantage point for observations of the earth. And whatever disadvantages they may have, compared with high synchronous orbits, for astronomical, astrophysical, meteorological and other scientific work may easily be compensated by the fact that low orbits are far more economical to attain.

The kind of space "business" beyond the moderate payload and low orbital altitude capability of the re-usable launch vehicle described here must be expected to be of rather low traffic density for the next decade or so. For such more-demanding missions—with very heavy payloads or leading to destinations much farther away from earth—nonrecoverable launch vehicles, like the Saturn V rocket developed for the Apollo lunar landing program, are likely to continue to be a better bet for years to come.

III. SAFETY IN SPACE

These Spacecraft say "Ouch!"

Three giant Pegasus satellites, all launched during 1965 and still working at this writing, are closing a gap in our knowledge about the hazards of meteoroids to our astronauts and their spacecraft.

The Pegasus satellites are reporting the first observations ever made, at close hand, of the abundance of meteoric particles that can penetrate metal as thick as 1/60 of an inch. Because these particles are infrequent, compared to smaller and less-penetrating ones, a meaningful count in a reasonable time takes a huge collecting area. Hence a Pegasus has a wing-like meteoroid-detecting surface of ninety-six-foot span.

What we call "meteoroids" are pieces of matter hurtling through space, regardless of size. They become "meteors" if they enter our atmosphere. "Meteorites" are those parts of meteoroids which reach the ground unconsumed. Meteoroids come in sizes from a dust speck ("micro-meteoroids") to a city block and more. The biggest are few and far between. Specks too tiny to puncture a space vehicle's skin hit a Gemini-size craft many times a day. It is the stuff of intermediate size that concerns a space-vehicle designer.

Particles of only a few thousandths of a gram, whizzing at fifteen to twenty miles a second, can penetrate a spacecraft's wall or a rocket's tank. They constitute a definite risk. If they puncture a tank or gas compartment, the result can be a serious leak—or, possibly, explosive rupture of a tank under pressure. Heat from their impact may ignite certain propellants, or materials in a crew compartment's oxygen-enriched atmosphere. And meteoroid-caused "spalling"—ejection of flying fragments of a spacecraft's interior wall surface—can form secondary projectiles endangering the crew and vital parts of their craft's equipment. Determined and costly efforts have therefore been made by NASA to appraise the meteoroid hazard.

Before the space age, optical observation of shooting stars had yielded considerable data on the abundance of meteoroids, and radar observation later added more. But these methods detected meteoroids no smaller than about a thousandth of a gram.

Beginning with Explorer I, the first U.S. satellite, space probes were equipped with microphonic and electrical devices to record the impact of meteoric dust. Particles as small as a million-millionth (1/1,000,000,000,000) of a gram were detectable. But the collecting devices offered a target area of only a few square inches—rarely hit by meteoroids big enough to interest space-vehicle designers.

The Pegasus project's aim was to fill the void of data on meteoroids weighing between about a thousandth and a 10-millionth of a gram. For launching the big 33,000-pound Pegasus satellites, the Saturn I rocket proved well suited. NASA's Marshall Space Flight Center, responsible for developing Saturn I, was also placed in charge of developing the Pegasus spacecraft.

The wings of a Pegasus, which unfold in orbit, are covered on both sides with aluminum plates that serve as targets for meteoroids. This provides a total collecting surface of more than two thousand square feet—the floor area of a large one-family house. Most of the aluminum plates are 1/60 of an inch thick. Others have a thickness of 1/120 of an inch; a few, of 1/600 of an inch. This enables a Pegasus to register meteoroids of three different degrees of penetrating power.

Pegasus has an electronic system whose main function is to say "ouch" every time a hit occurs—and say it in such a way that the signal received on the ground can be intelligently interpreted. Beneath each aluminum plate is a film of plastic, coated on the other side with copper. This aluminum-plastic-copper sandwich, forming an electric capacitor, is charged to forty volts.

Each time a meteoroid punctures the aluminum, material vaporized by the impact momentarily short-circuits the capacitor—and a memory system records the event. On ground command, Pegasus reads out all data. This gives a count of the meteoroids that have pierced a known area of each thickness in a known time.

Since the Pegasus satellites are still collecting data, their findings are not yet complete. However, a chart made public by NASA summarizes what they have told us in their first ten months of operation.

According to this preliminary summary, the yearly meteoroid punctures in a square foot of aluminum sheet, on the outside of a spacecraft in low orbit, can be expected to number somewhere near:

7, for 1/600-inch sheet
0.6, for 1/120-inch sheet
0.13, for 1/60-inch sheet

Now, an intact ten-foot sphere, which has a surface area of 314 square feet, could safely withstand an internal pressure of one atmosphere and provide an earthlike environment for astronauts in outer space, if made of 1/60-inch aluminum. But the Pegasus findings indicate that it would be punctured about forty times a year. So that wall thickness, for a manned spacecraft, would expose a crew to serious meteoroid hazard during extended space flights.

Fortunately, spacecraft capable of re-entry into the atmosphere —like Mercury, Gemini, and Apollo—have a healthy padding of heat protection that greatly reduces the penetration hazard. But space vehicles and space stations without re-entry capability are under development for extended operating times in space. So adequate meteoroid protection is becoming more important than ever. With better meteoroid data, designers will be able to provide enough "armor" to reduce the risk from meteoroids in any given space mission to a figure commensurate with other risks that must be accepted.

The gap in our knowledge is not yet completely closed. We'd like to know the abundance of meteoroids that can penetrate aluminum sheets as thick as 1/25 and 1/10 of an inch, figures representative of many space-vehicle structures. NASA has announced that it plans to tackle the problem of that remaining gap during the coming years. Satellites still larger than Pegasus, or a greater number of Pegasus-size satellites in orbit at once, could be possible ways.

What It Takes to Survive in Space

To survive in outer space an astronaut must have specialized equipment and supplies in addition to food and drink. He needs:

A pressurized spacecraft cabin, with means for replenishing oxygen, removing carbon dioxide and odor, and controlling temperature and humidity.

A contour seat, for the high accelerations and decelerations encountered during launch, mid-course maneuvers, and re-entry.

A pressure suit, as protection in case of cabin-pressure loss, and as mandatory equipment if the mission ever requires the astronaut to go outside his spacecraft.

Sanitary accommodations in accordance with the duration of the mission.

Some radiation protection, dependent on the length of the mission and the flight profile. For example, an extended stay in the Van Allen Belts, or a long interplanetary voyage, demands more radiation protection than a low-altitude earth-orbit flight, which can be recalled at short notice in case of a dangerously powerful solar flare.

For very long outer-space flights, a degree of bodily mobility is also likely to be necessary. Some equipment for physical exercise —possibly of the familiar coil-spring kind—may prove indispensable, too.

Among space medical men, opinions still vary as to whether the zero-gravity condition, always prevailing during the unpowered stretches of a space voyage, will turn out to be acceptable for extended periods. Some believe the astronauts will need an "artificial G environment" in such cases. One scheme would provide a separate "reconditioning capsule" attached by a cable to the ship's main body and slowly spinning around it; in this capsule, centrifugal force would then simulate gravity.

It is quite interesting to consider a spaceman's growing requirements for an artificial atmosphere as he ascends to higher and higher altitudes. The average person needs some life-support equipment above about three miles. At this altitude, along with decreased *total* atmospheric pressure, the *partial* pressure of the air's oxygen has sunk so low that the lungs cannot absorb enough of it. Hypoxia, or oxygen deficiency in the blood, results. Breathing pure oxygen (at the same reduced total atmospheric pressure) raises the oxygen partial pressure, and thus a simple oxygen mask provides a ready remedy.

At an altitude of 4½ miles, the unprotected human body faces another difficulty. By now, atmospheric pressure has dropped to a point where the nitrogen dissolved in our blood starts bubbling out. The physics of this is identical with what happens when we open, and thus depressurize, a warm Coke bottle. The effects, however, are decidedly more severe. Some nitrogen bubbles, as the pulsating bloodstream washes them through the body, may get trapped in corners such as elbow and knee joints. As the ambient pressure keeps falling, the trapped bubbles expand further and may block off an artery. This causes painful aeroembolism, better known as the "bends." Thus, beyond a limit of 4½ miles or so, pressure cabins or pressure suits (at least, partial-pressure suits), or both, must be provided.

Ten miles up is another biological milestone. By now the atmospheric pressure has become as little as the combined partial pressures of water vapor and carbon dioxide, two substances always present in our lungs. No matter how much pure oxygen we try to breathe, the air sacs of the lungs are now completely filled with this mixture of water vapor and carbon dioxide, and no oxygen can enter the blood stream. This condition is called anoxia.

Just a little higher up, the unprotected, tortured body would virtually boil over. At an altitude of twelve miles or so the air is so thin that the boiling point of our body fluid drops to around 100 degrees F., which is about our body temperature. Bubbles now form wherever body fluids are openly exposed on surface areas of the body, such as the mucous linings of the mouth and eyes.

While all these milestones of increasing biological hazards have tremendous practical significance in aviation, their importance for spacecraft is actually quite limited. A spacecraft's life-support system must be designed for an extended stay in completely airless outer space, anyway. In less than one minute a manned rocket clears the lower atmosphere, so there is not much chance of taking advantage of the less-demanding conditions prevailing there. Hence, it does not matter too much to the designer whether his craft is five or fifty thousand miles high. He has to provide adequate life support for the most demanding condition, a perfect vacuum outside.

We must distinguish between three different types of life-support systems: open, closed, and a crossbreed called semiclosed.

An open system simply delivers fresh air or oxygen to a breathing mask, and vents exhaled air overboard. It makes no attempt to retain and recirculate the unused oxygen—or the seventy-nine percent nitrogen in exhaled air. The aqualung is an example of an open life-support system, using air. The oxygen-mask system in unpressurized aircraft is an open system using pure oxygen.

A closed life-support system attempts to duplicate in capsule form the complete miraculous "ecological system" that nature operates on earth: The carbon dioxide that man and beast exhale is absorbed by plants and helps them grow and develop through an intricate process called photosynthesis—the fundamental process of life on earth. Light energy from the sun converts the carbon dioxide into plant-building carbohydrates, while oxygen is released into the air. Men and animals breathe this oxygen, and eat the plants and the fruits they bear, while their body wastes fertilize the soil on which the plants grow.

Very promising attempts have been made to duplicate nature's grand scheme in the laboratory. Most experimenters use certain strains of algae as the plants for the ecological cycle.

Obviously the advantage of the open life-support system lies in its simplicity. But it is very wasteful, and the weight of the air or unused oxygen vented overboard becomes prohibitive for space-flight missions of more than a few hours.

The closed system on the other hand is complicated and relatively heavy. But it is ideally suited for long operating periods, because it puts the sun to work to enable us to reclaim virtually all of the wastes. We can expect such closed systems to be used in

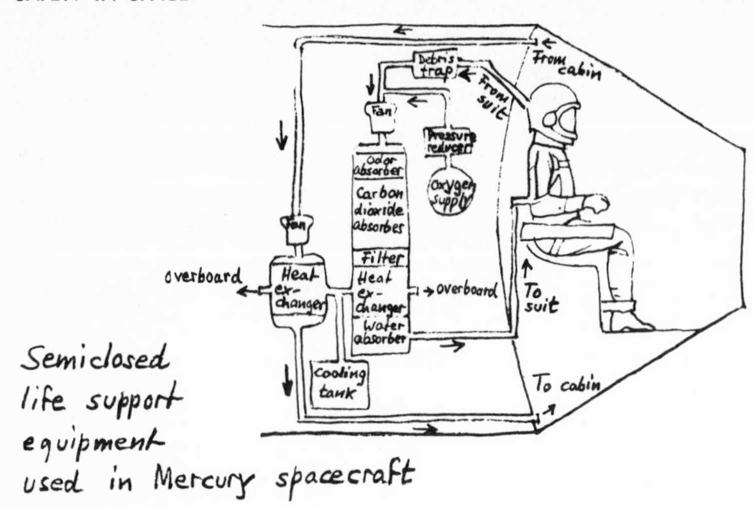

Semiclosed life support equipment used in Mercury spacecraft

manned interplanetary expeditions, and at a permanent base on the moon.

For the Mercury spacecraft's flights, of up to several days, a semiclosed system using a pure-oxygen atmosphere was selected. This system is best explained with the help of my sketch (which I made from a description published by the maker, The Garrett Corporation of Los Angeles).

As shown, there are two almost independent recirculation cycles —for the pressurized cabin and the pressurized space suit. Water-cooled heat exchangers, inserted in both cycles, dissipate the heat generated by the astronaut himself and by all the electrical gear. A supply of oxygen—carried in gaseous form at 7,500-pound pressure—replenishes the suit cycle with fresh oxygen, to the same extent that an absorber removes exhaled carbon dioxide.

This system proved entirely adequate for the limited duration of the Mercury flight missions. Many medical experts believe, however, that for flights of much longer duration it will be necessary to replace the semiclosed oxygen system with a semiclosed air system —that is, a system where the oxygen is diluted with nitrogen or other inert gases. According to Soviet reports, the man-carrying Vostok spacecraft all used semiclosed air systems.

Beating the Perils of Manned Space Flight

What are the most dangerous moments, I have been asked, in a manned space flight? A layman may expect a melodramatic answer. Space-vehicle designers and mission planners strive for precisely the opposite. They seek to provide against hazards in such a way that no particular event or situation in a manned space flight can be singled out as especially risky to the astronauts or their mission.

True, there are critical events, any one of which can conceivably spell disaster. In an Apollo lunar-landing mission, these critical events will include:

1. Launch preparation.
2. Takeoff.
3. Staging–the detaching of exhausted rocket stages and ignition of next-higher ones.
4. Restart, from parking orbit around the earth, to head for the moon.
5. Separation and transposition of the Apollo Command and Service Module (CSM), resulting in joining it to the Landing Module (LM), as well as subsequent separation of the exhausted Saturn V third stage.
6. De-boost (slowing by retrofire) into lunar orbit.
7. Descent maneuver of the LM.
8. Touchdown on the moon.
9. Takeoff from the moon.
10. Rendezvous of LM with CSM in lunar orbit.
11. Departure from lunar orbit to return to earth.
12. Re-entry into earth's atmosphere.
13. Parachute-deployment sequence.
14. Recovery from ocean.

By methods we shall come to, the hazards of all these situations can be soberly appraised and reduced to a minimum. Resulting safeguards will aim to assure an Apollo mission's success from start to finish. And, even if the mission should fail, they are still to provide for bringing the astronauts back safely.

Suppose, for example, that while an Apollo spacecraft's crew are orbiting the moon before landing, they find that pressure is

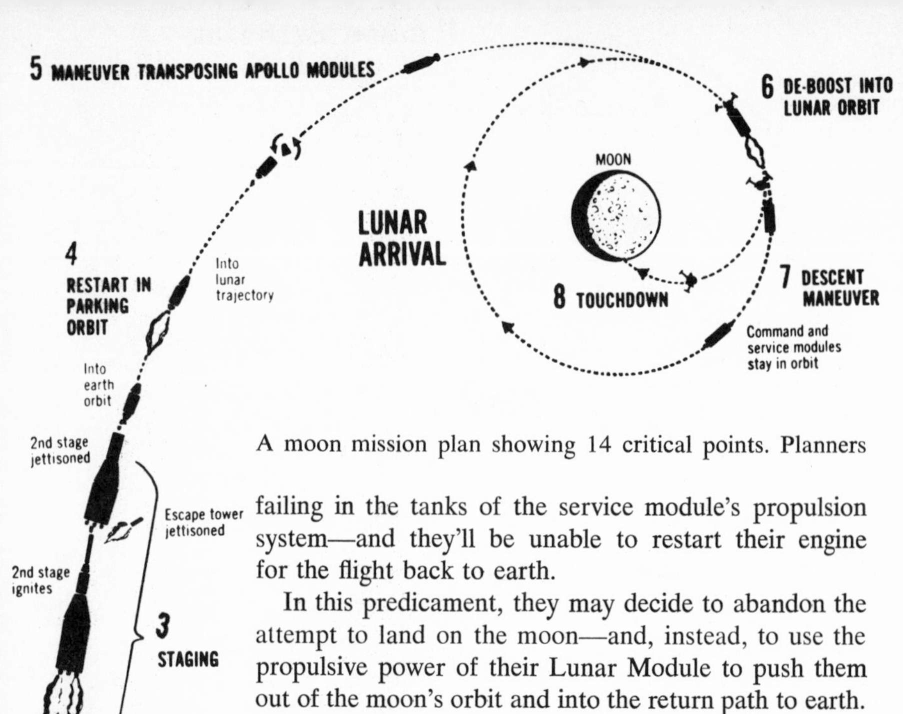

A moon mission plan showing 14 critical points. Planners

failing in the tanks of the service module's propulsion system—and they'll be unable to restart their engine for the flight back to earth.

In this predicament, they may decide to abandon the attempt to land on the moon—and, instead, to use the propulsive power of their Lunar Module to push them out of the moon's orbit and into the return path to earth. This decision obviously would result in only partial success for the mission—but it would give the crew an excellent chance for survival.

For an overall appraisal of space-flight hazards, we have as yet no accident statistics to guide us. Fortunately, all our Mercury and Gemini astronauts have returned hale and hearty from their missions. But it would be unrealistic to assume that manned-space-flight activities will go on forever without accidents and tragedies. So a vital part of the job of developing space vehicles and planning missions is to try to minimize the risks, through analysis of all potentially hazardous situations, equipment failures, and human errors.

In aviation, the years have brought a sizable body of accident data, and many ways of analyzing it have become possible. Comparisons have been made of accidents in scheduled and unscheduled airline flights, other commercial flying, military aviation, and private flying. Causes of accidents have been broken down into cases of equipment failure (such as engine trouble or fire aboard) and of pilot error (including bad navigation and venturing unpre-

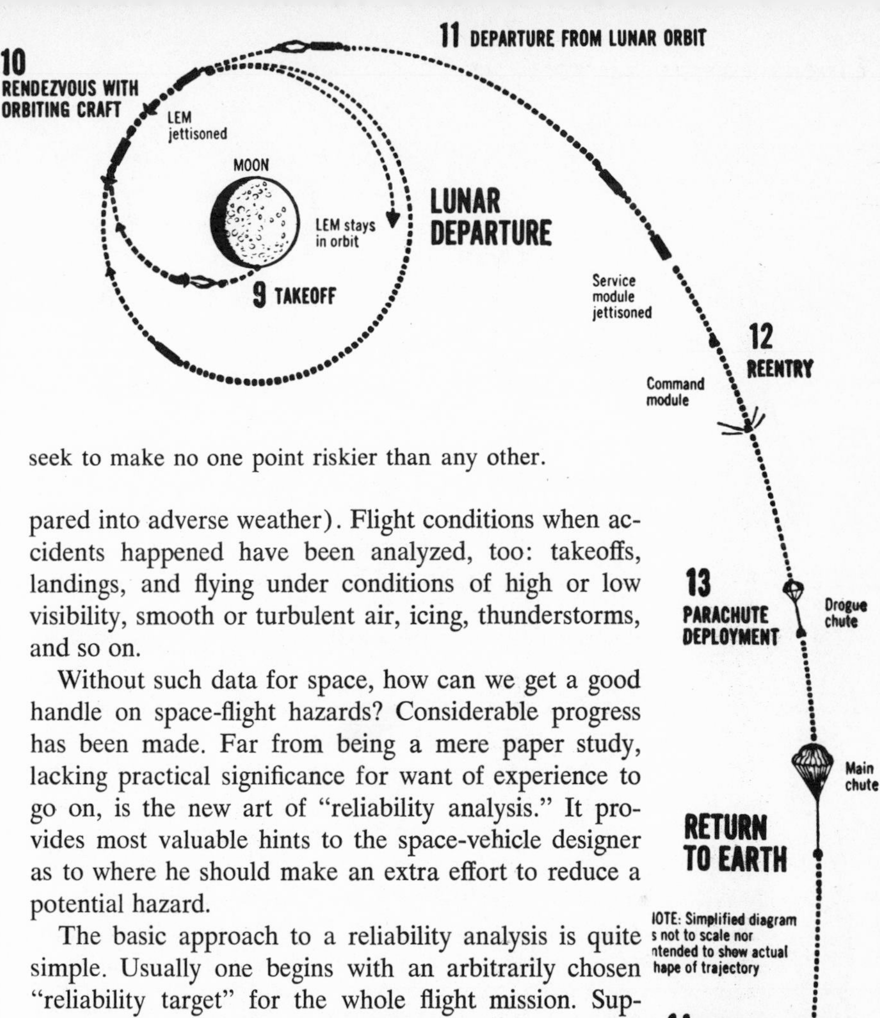

seek to make no one point riskier than any other.

pared into adverse weather). Flight conditions when accidents happened have been analyzed, too: takeoffs, landings, and flying under conditions of high or low visibility, smooth or turbulent air, icing, thunderstorms, and so on.

Without such data for space, how can we get a good handle on space-flight hazards? Considerable progress has been made. Far from being a mere paper study, lacking practical significance for want of experience to go on, is the new art of "reliability analysis." It provides most valuable hints to the space-vehicle designer as to where he should make an extra effort to reduce a potential hazard.

The basic approach to a reliability analysis is quite simple. Usually one begins with an arbitrarily chosen "reliability target" for the whole flight mission. Suppose this is an Apollo-Saturn flight to the moon and back, including a lunar landing. Let us assume—and my figure is for illustration only—that a reliability target of 90 percent is set for the entire mission, including safe return to earth. That would mean that nine tries out of ten must succeed.

We now parcel out this overall reliability target to the three propulsion stages and the one guidance stage of the Saturn V launch vehicle, and to the three modules of the Apollo spacecraft riding in the Saturn V's nose. Suppose—again, solely for illustration—we allot a reliability requirement of ninety-nine percent to *each* of these seven elements of the whole space vehicle.

According to the laws of probability, the overall reliability of the entire space vehicle will then be the product obtained by multiplying together seven .99's, which is .93 or 93 percent. This betters our overall 90-percent target by 3 percent, which we may allot to hazards unrelated to equipment, such as unfavorable terrain for the touchdown on the moon or a piloting error during the rendezvous in lunar orbit.

Now we can go on to the next step and see if the booster stages and spacecraft modules really offer the 99-percent reliability demanded of them. This calls for "qualification-testing" all critical components of a stage or module, under environmental conditions more severe than the actual flight environment of a space vehicle, before they are admitted to the assembly. The tests are applied, not to parts of any actual space vehicle, but to similar pieces from the same manufacturing line.

Often this procedure shows that certain parts of a stage simply cannot be made reliable enough to pass the severe tests. Invariably the answer is redundancy—provision of a back-up component that can take over the job if the other one fails.

Redundant components are nothing new in engineering. Your car has two headlights, in case one goes out. Large aircraft have two or more engines and several independent radios. In manned space flight, with its unprecedented demands for near-perfection, providing redundancy has become a highly sophisticated art.

Wherever advisable and possible, Project Apollo-Saturn provides redundancy not only in components but also in alternate choices of operational procedures. Thus, midcourse navigation between earth and moon can be performed by astronomical navigation aboard the spacecraft, as well as by radio and radar tracking from the ground. Life support can be provided either by the crew compartment's pressurizing system or, if that fails, by the astronauts' space suits.

Usually the reliability-allotment game is played through several times before the figures are finally cast in concrete. The higher the target is set, the greater will be the weight and complexity of the system, until handicaps offset further gains.

Reliability requirements for crew survival and mission success are by no means identical. For instance, if the launch vehicle develops serious trouble during boosted ascent, the mission will be lost anyhow. But we are still faced with enabling the crew to abort safely and return to the earth's surface. The reliability to be expected of various conceivable abort modes, during a space-flight mission, can be quite different.

After all humanly possible precautions are taken, whatever hazards remain in a manned space flight result from the overall complexity of manned space missions and the vehicles needed to fly them. When all is said and done, we still have to live with the fact that every time a space vehicle takes off, there are hundreds of thousands of not-so-perfect human beings involved in the act.

Since the dawn of the space age, many people active in our national space program have been involved in travel and household accidents. Even some of our astronauts have not been spared. So, in appraising the overall risk of flying to the moon, we should not completely disregard the hazard of the astronauts' travels to their training stations and their final automobile ride to the launch pad.

Can an Astronaut Bail Out and Live?

There are times when an astronaut in trouble can bail out, but it depends on the situation. Obviously an astronaut, once he has been injected into an orbit around the earth, cannot simply abandon a stricken spacecraft and live. Equipped with nothing but his space suit and a space-walker's reaction pistol, he cannot "retro" himself out of the orbit and hope to survive a blazing re-entry into the atmosphere, without the protection of capsule and heat shield.

On the other hand, a bail-out during the first thirty or forty seconds of his booster rocket's ascent would subject an astronaut to no more severe an aerodynamic shock than in parachute ejection from a fast aircraft.

Because of the wide spectrum of flight conditions encountered during a typical orbital mission, the designers of the Mercury capsule, our first manned spacecraft, decided to adhere to the ground rule that the astronaut shall stay with the ship, come what may. Instead of providing emergency means for the astronaut to eject himself into what might be a marginal or deadly environment, they furnished all conceivable safety features to bring the capsule itself to earth intact, with the astronaut safe inside. In Project Gemini, by contrast, the astronauts can eject themselves from their spacecraft during the early portions of the launch phase (*See* Chapter 25 "Abort Methods for Astronauts in Trouble").

In case of a sudden emergency during the launch phase, the boosted ascent into orbit, the main requirement for safe capsule recovery is a suitable mechanism for rapid separation of the capsule from the boost rocket.

In Project Mercury this mechanism consisted of a Launch Escape Tower extending forward from the top of the capsule, with a powerful short-burning solid-fuel escape rocket in its tip. Upon activation by the astronaut, the escape rocket would be fired while a set of explosive bolts would sever the capsule from the aborting Atlas rocket. Simultaneously the Atlas engines would be shut down—and the escape rocket would hurl the spacecraft and its occupant away from the booster with a brutal 20-G blast. The main purpose of this escape rocket was to put a safe distance, as quickly as possible, between the spacecraft and the stricken booster—which, like a jet plane hit by enemy fire, conceivably might explode at any moment. In case a dangerous launch vehicle fire developed while the Atlas rocket was still sitting on its launch pad, the Mercury escape rocket was powerful enough to carry the capsule to a safe altitude for deployment of the capsule parachute.

About 2½ minutes after lift-off, with the two Atlas *booster* engines already dropped off and the flight continuing under *sustainer* engine power, the Launch Escape Tower is jettisoned. By now, the Mercury-Atlas combination has risen above the sensible or perceptible atmosphere, and a failure in the complex Atlas control system would no longer lead to structural breakup and resulting explosion. Aerodynamic forces during an emergency separation have likewise become negligible.

As a result, separation can now be effected simply by shutting off the Atlas sustainer engine—and gently pushing the capsule away from the Atlas with the help of a set of rather weak "posigrade" rockets. Since the spacecraft has not yet attained orbital speed, it will soon drop back into the denser layers of the atmosphere. The astronaut must therefore turn his capsule around so

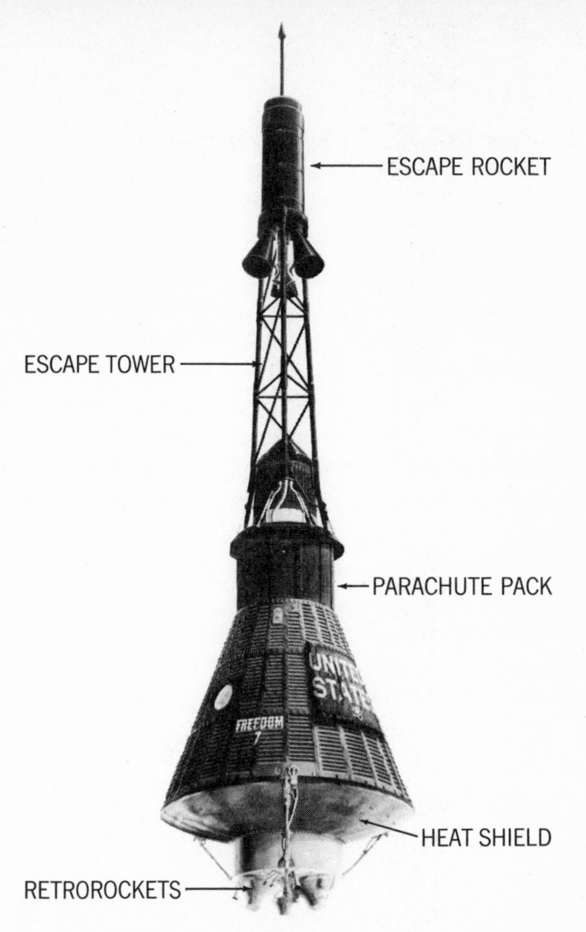

The Mercury capsule provides an astronaut with these means to bail out or end orbiting prematurely.

that its blunt heat shield will be facing the onrushing air. This places him in a safe condition for re-entry.

About five minutes after lift-off, if no emergency has developed during the ascent phase, the Atlas-Mercury system goes into orbit. Immediately the capsule is separated from its booster and turned around. This, again, puts it in a safe re-entry position.

But while re-entry into the atmosphere is the automatic consequence of shutting off Atlas power in an emergency at *suborbital* speed, return into the atmosphere from *orbital* flight always requires a separate retro-fire maneuver to reduce the initial orbital speed. The rocket power for this maneuver is provided by the so-called retropack strapped to the heat shield of the Mercury capsule —the same retropack that normally ends an orbital flight.

Thus, emergency descent from an orbit is simply a premature termination of the original flight plan.

Abort Methods for Astronauts in Trouble

When trouble strikes a manned spacecraft in the "launch phase" between earth and orbit, the urgent thing is to get the astronauts safely back to the ground. Several ways to do it have been developed in the course of our space program. They have notable differences, both in the mechanics of the escape method and in how it is triggered into action—as is illustrated by the evolution of escape procedures in our successive Mercury, Gemini, and Apollo projects.

During launch preparation and the first fifty or sixty seconds of a manned space flight, the use of ejection seats like those of military aircraft is still possible. The Gemini spacecraft actually provides this means of escape.

At higher speeds, however, ejection into the slipstream becomes out of the question. And at near-orbital velocities, although the force of the onrushing air subsides as the launch vehicle climbs above the atmosphere, re-entry heating poses another insurmountable obstacle for unprotected bailout.

For these reasons, astronaut emergency procedures during the launch phase are based upon the ground rule: Stay in your spacecraft, come what may, and ride down with the ship! Escape from a Gemini launch by ejection seats during the first minute is the only departure from this rule.

The one-man Mercury capsule and our new three-man Apollo craft have no ejection seats at all. In case of serious booster difficulties during the ascent through the atmosphere, a powerful short-burning solid-propellant rocket jerks the capsule away from the trouble-stricken booster—and to a safe distance, lest the booster explode. Parachutes then ease the spacecraft, with the astronauts inside, all the way to the ground.

Gemini astronauts, too, stay in their spacecraft in case of an emergency after the first minute of flight. Firing its own retrorockets in salvo (or, later, its thrusters), the two-man capsule

Escape rocket for the 3-man Apollo moon capsule shown upside-down on its test stand in a flaming trial.

separates from the shutdown booster and a parachute lowers it to earth.

When a multistage launch vehicle takes off from its launch pad, and shoves the manned spacecraft in its nose into orbit within a few minutes, large numbers of highly complex systems are activated, turned off, and detached in rapid sequence. Whenever trouble hits during the launch phase, it is liable to hit fast. In certain cases it may even hit so fast that there might not be time for the astronauts to consult their display panels and make a decision.

Automatic abort has seemed the only answer in such cases. Yet it is not very popular with astronauts.

The Mercury program did use an entirely automatic crew-safety system. Symptoms of impending launch-vehicle failure were sensed and wired to trigger automatic abort. The booster engines would be cut off, the spacecraft would separate, and the escape rocket would be fired to hurl it safely clear. This in turn would trigger subsequent events, such as the jettisoning of the escape tower, and parachute deployment.

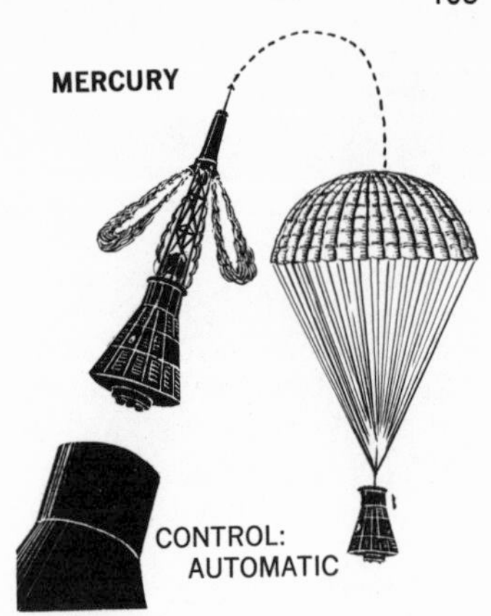

Mercury escape system—the capsule is automatically yanked out of danger by the escape rocket linked to it by the tower, and then, jettisoning the tower, descends on a parachute with the astronaut inside.

The Gemini crew-safety system, in contrast, is entirely manual. The various indications of potential launch-vehicle failure are displayed to the flight crew. But it is the crew's decision whether or not to initiate abort action. On at least one occasion, a Gemini command pilot did actually decide against heeding the abort advice flashed on his display panel:

During an attempt to launch Gemini 6 December 12, 1965, the two engines of the Titan booster's first stage shut down without lifting the vehicle off the pad. Due to the engine vibrations, an electrical plug had prematurely dropped out of the still-tied-down booster.

This plug disconnection—since it normally would have occurred only through the movement of the rocket after actual lift-

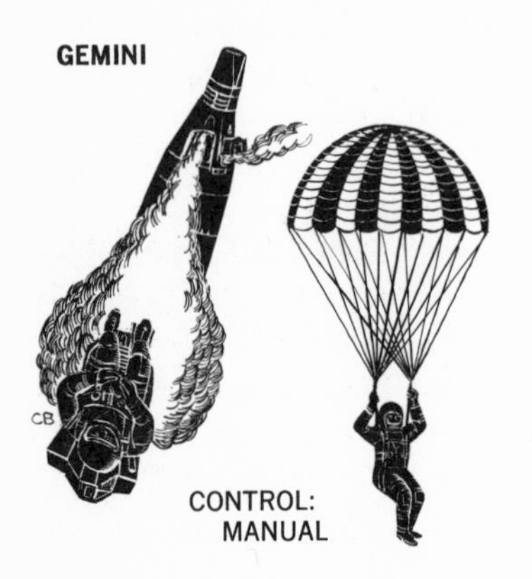

Gemini escape system uses manual-controlled ejection seats to abandon capsule from 0-15,000 feet. Astronauts swing down on individual chutes. Above 15,000 feet, astronauts stay with the capsule and bring it down on its own chute.

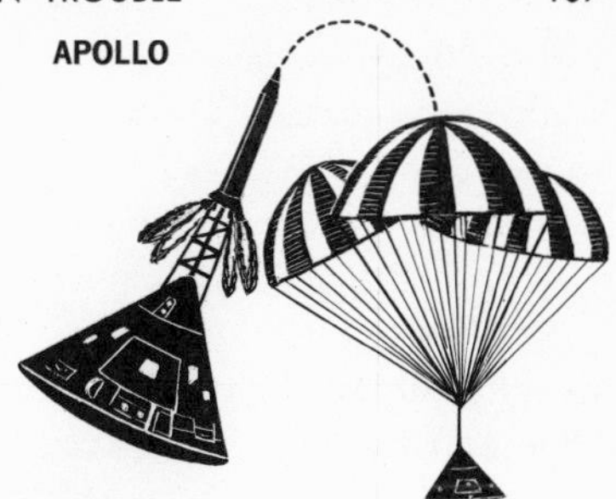

Apollo escape system uses escape rocket to hurl whole capsule away from disabled booster, but reserves automatic triggering for fast-developing emergencies and adopts manual control by astronauts for use in other emergencies.

off—started the on-board timer and the guidance and control system, and made the on-board electrical logic system "believe" that the bird was in flight. A few seconds later a timer in the ground-support equipment, not having received a tailgrab-release signal within a specified period of time, shut down the booster engines. The crew-safety system went on to conclude, quite logically, that a dire emergency demanding immediate abort had arisen—apparently the "rocketborne" vehicle, its engines failing, was about to fall back on its pad.

In effect this advised the two astronauts to pull D-shaped rings actuating their ejection seats. Hurtling about three hundred feet high and eight hundred feet sideward, they would then swing to earth on their parachutes.

But the command pilot, Capt. Walter Schirra, was sure the bird had never left the pad. He disregarded the warning signal. His correct split-second decision attested to his presence of mind—and to the fact that there is indeed much merit in giving man a role in the decision-making.

In the Apollo-Saturn program, an approach halfway between Mercury and Gemini has been taken. Vehicle-failure situations that can be expected to lead only slowly to catastrophic conditions are indicated on a display panel, and the decision to execute abort is left to the flight crew. Failure situations that are bound to lead rapidly to disaster will trigger automatic abort.

Whether automatic or manual, crew-safety systems must be as simple as possible. Simplicity enhances assurance that the system will really work—and also reduces the hazard of a false alarm that could unnecessarily abort a perfect flight. The most effective way to simplify the system is to make it sense the result of a malfunction, rather than the malfunction itself.

One of the most critical situations arises if one of a space rocket's swivel-mounted engines should suddenly go "hard over," or tilt to an extreme angle. For steering, rocket engines are deflected back and forth a few degrees by hydraulic pistons ("actuators"), according to signals received from the control computer. A "hard over" could conceivably result from either an electrical or a hydraulic failure.

For instance, by sensing the movements of the eight actuators, which swivel the four movable engines of the Saturn V's first stage, one could provide "hard-over" warning indicators, but this would be a rather complex installation.

Instead, we might disregard the actuators and simply sense the whole vehicle's turning rate and angle of attack. What concerns us is not an engine's deflection, but the result—the vehicle's rapid turn, and the build-up of an excessive angle of attack that might cause its structural breakup.

Considerations like these have led to the following crew-safety system for the Saturn V/Apollo moon-rocket vehicle:

> Automatic abort will be triggered if two or more rocket engines of the Saturn V shut down after lift-off; or if the vehicle builds up a rotation rate, in the pitch or yaw plane, of faster than five degrees per second; or if the vehicle starts rolling faster than 20 degrees per second.
>
> Manual abort is executed at the command pilot's discretion. He has at his disposal the following cues: angle-of-attack display, in pitch and yaw planes; turning rates in pitch, yaw, and roll, as indicated by the spacecraft's own guidance system; and an abort request radioed up by the flight director, who takes his cues mainly from telemetered data.

In case of trouble after a manned spacecraft is in orbit, the only conceivable way out—short of future orbital rescue efforts by other spacecraft—is to fire the retrorocket system and re-enter the atmosphere. If possible, the astronauts will defer their retrorocket maneuver until the resulting re-entry path will end near a recovery ship. Even if a medical emergency should befall a crew member, the 18,000-m.p.h. capsule will always be the fastest ambulance available.

The Problem of Space Rescue

Sooner or later, we must be prepared to hear an SOS from the crew of a manned spacecraft in distress. What can we do to rescue the astronauts?

To date, our safety record in manned space flight has been outstanding. High standards of mission planning and control and of rocket and spacecraft design, plus superb astronaut selection and training, have spared us a space-flight tragedy. But as our objectives get bolder, as missions become more frequent and longer, and as ever-larger crews become involved in them, the chances are high that statistics will one day catch up with us. The close shave that the Gemini 8 crew had in March, 1966, when a runaway thruster threw their craft into a violent tumbling motion, has spurred demand for an active Space Rescue Program.

In many ways the problem of space rescue resembles the age-old problem of rescuing sailors from the sea. Emergencies may be much the same—equipment failure, illness or injury of a crew member, fire or explosion, a navigational error, or collision. The resulting space-rescue tasks, like sea-rescue operations, may range from the relatively easy to the near-impossible.

A spacecraft crew marooned in a low orbit around the earth by retrorocket failure is in a situation comparable with that of an offshore fishing party that cannot get the boat's engine restarted. The yacht can request assistance from a Coast Guard cutter alerted by ship-to-shore radio. Even if the boat is rapidly sinking or afire lifeboats or life rafts offer an excellent chance of survival. For orbital flight, to be sure, neither Coast Guard cutters nor lifeboats are yet in existence, but they are entirely within reach of existing technology and may indeed become available in the not-too-distant future.

At the other extreme in the range of space-rescue difficulty are future voyages across vast and empty space to other planets. Rescue from mishaps on such extended missions can only be based on the general pattern set by the great explorers of the sailing-ship age. When Columbus lost his *Santa Maria* in a shipwreck at newly discovered Hispaniola, he transferred himself and her crew to the *Nina* and *Pinta* for the return voyage.

Obviously, a capability for space rescue did not and could not exist for the pioneering orbital flights. Our Mercury program was designed to prove that man could live and perform in space with his proficiency not greatly impaired by zero gravity. It remained for subsequent Gemini flights to show the feasibility of orbital rendezvous and docking, a prerequisite for any scheme of rescue from the ground. And even the Gemini successes in rendezvous and docking do not mean that all we need to do for ground-based rescue is to hold a Gemini poised in constant readiness on its Titan II launch pad at Cape Kennedy. The problem is not as simple as that.

An orbit is fixed in space. The launch pad at Cape Kennedy whirls around the earth's axis once every twenty-four hours. For a rendezvous to be possible, an ascending "chaser" rocket's course must lie in about the same plane as that of its previously orbited target—and that will happen only if it is launched during infrequent and brief periods, called launch windows.

Astronauts in the trouble-stricken target spacecraft may therefore have to wait many hours before the "Coast Guard cutter" can leave port. Bad weather, in the launch or emergency-abort area, and other factors may further delay a rescue effort.

Extremely powerful rockets such as Saturn V theoretically could execute a dogleg maneuver from a launch at the Cape into a target orbit in a different plane. This could substantially prolong the launch windows—or, to put it the other way around, could shorten the time the party in distress would have to wait for rescue. But, aside from the high cost of such a rescue operation, the time required to get such a large and complex launch vehicle off the ground might well offset the gain of the wider launch window.

Not every orbiting spacecraft, unable to de-orbit because of retrorocket failure, will actually be in a hurry for rescue. As long as oxygen for breathing holds out, the crew can wait until help arrives.

Unfortunately, however, a careful analysis of space-rescue needs

Space Parachute, a Douglas concept, features an ejection seat with retrorocket for de-orbiting. Then the conical drag skirt deploys for self-stabilizing re-entry and landing cushioned by crushable nose. Because of the light load per unit area no heat shield is needed.

shows that a substantial number of potential emergencies are likely to be urgent. If the crew does not get help at once, it will be too late.

A fire in a spacecraft is an example. The artificial atmosphere of present-day spacecraft consists of pure oxygen. An electrical short may cause a flash fire, disabling the craft's delicate electrical network within seconds. While the astronauts may be protected by their space suits and may extinguish the fire by depressurizing their cabin their craft may not be inhabitable any longer.

The same result may follow penetration of the spacecraft by a heavy meteoroid; collision of two spacecraft in an attempted rendezvous maneuver; pollution of the cabin atmosphere with offensive or toxic fumes released, for instance, by rupture of a hydraulic-pressure sensing line; and a mishap with a nuclear electric-power source creating a radiation hazard in the craft.

The urgency of spaceflight hazards like these has led many planners to propose the time-honored idea of the lifeboat as the best answer. For outer space, of course, the first and foremost requirement of a lifeboat is to furnish the shipwrecked astronauts

Separable Shelter (*left*), by North American, expands to hold 5-15 men and can serve as a life raft for future large space vehicles. Rocket self-propulsion can boost it higher into a longer-lived orbit that allows more time for rescuers to arrive.

Emergency Cocoon (*right*), by General Electric, shelters ship-wrecked astronaut in an inflated fabric ball, heat-insulated by outer layers of aluminized plastic. Thin silicone-rubber lining retains oxygen carried for breathing but lets unwanted carbon dioxide and water vapor escape.

with a shelter containing a breathable atmosphere away from their stricken spacecraft.

Space lifeboats to shelter astronauts temporarily, while they await rescue from the ground, are envisioned by some designers. To this category belongs General Electric's Emergency Cocoon, an inflatable spherical shelter with heat insulation and provision for ridding exhaled air of carbon dioxide. North American Aviation proposes Separable Shelters, also stowable and inflatable, but a little more elaborate; they are equipped to propel themselves from lower into higher and therefore safer orbits.

Other suggestions call for lifeboats with full re-entry capability. In this class belong the Douglas Space Parachute and General Electric's MOOSE (for Manned Orbital Operations Safety Equipment). Both fold for storage in a spacecraft and both combine the characteristics of a liferaft, a space-suit overcoat, and a cocoon.

Devices like these offer the obvious advantage of independence of ground-launched help. However, safe re-entry and descent to earth do not assure survival. An uncontrolled re-entry could land the space lifeboat in an inaccessible area or on a wind-swept ocean. Self-rescue devices must therefore be provided with com-

Self-rescue MOOSE, a General Electric idea, encases the astronaut in a plastic bag that fills with polyurethane foam to assume re-entry shape. The astronaut uses a retrorocket to de-orbit, then discards it. The bag has a foldable heat shield for re-entry and a parachute that automatically unfurls itself for landing.

munications and tracking equipment, light beacons, and survival and flotation gear.

Will we be able to rescue future explorers stranded on the moon?

Our Apollo program provides the astronauts with a great variety of "abort options," should something go wrong during the many phases of a voyage to the moon and back. But if an early Apollo landing party were unable to return from the moon to the mother spacecraft left orbiting around it, any attempt to rescue them from the earth would simply come too late.

In an advanced stage of lunar-surface operation, however, things will be quite different. Just as Arctic explorers can survive an entire winter in the freezing cold, future lunar explorers can be provided with temporary shelters and enough supplies to await rescue for weeks or months, if need be. Moreover, just as Surveyor 1 soft-landed television equipment at a precisely predetermined spot on the moon, it is entirely feasible for unmanned craft to deliver everything needed for survival to a stranded lunar expedition of the future until a relief party can reach it. These supplies may be dispatched either from a lunar base or from the earth direct.

IV.
STATIONS IN SPACE

What Has Happened to the Manned Space Stations?

During the years before Sputnik several writers, including myself, predicted that one of the first objectives of manned space flight would be to establish one or more orbiting space stations.

Today we're busy building rockets and spacecraft to take men to the moon. We have been fabulously successful with Projects Mercury and Gemini and our advanced Saturn I rockets have shown that they can reliably haul more than twenty tons of payload into orbit. Yet little is heard of manned space stations. Why is that so?

Actually, the manned-space-station concept is just as exciting today as it was fifteen years ago. There is absolutely no doubt that the United States will have one or several such stations in orbit within a very few years. The reason a project for space station hasn't been pushed more aggressively is simply that only through the process of conducting actual manned-space-flight operations could we learn how to build a station that is best-suited to the various purposes it is supposed to serve.

Meanwhile, the Gemini program has provided a wealth of practical experience on which a sound concept of a space station can be based. For the first time Gemini flights demonstrated the feasibility of orbital rendezvous and docking, a maneuver necessary for the establishment of any space station that can be revisited and resupplied. Inside and outside of their spacecraft, Gemini astronauts performed a whole slew of scientific observations and experiments. All this gave us a better idea of how much more can be accomplished by a manned space station than by an automatic observatory in space.

Already we can foresee many tasks for which manned space stations can be immensely useful:

Astronomical and astrophysical studies of sun, moon, planets, and the surrounding universe. The advantages of a space station would be freedom from atmospheric turbulence and from the filtering effects of the earth's atmosphere on ultraviolet and other radiation.

Observations of the earth's surface for many purposes: population census-taking; continuous surveillance of crops and subsequent harvest predictions on a global scale; prospecting for oil and ores; oceanographic surveys on sea state, water temperature, and salinity, plankton distribution and the resulting distribution of sea life; weather forecasting; storm and flood warning; iceberg patrol; snowfall and water-resource management; prediction of volcanic eruptions and landslides; detection of forest fires; military reconnaissance; as well as navigational aid and traffic control for ships and aircraft.

Physical, medical, and life-sciences research. A space station is the ideal place for research on the effects of a number of conditions impossible to simulate on earth: prolonged weightlessness, space radiation of various types, a near-perfect vacuum of umlimited size.

Maintenance of complex space installations. Unmanned communications satellites are old hat, of course, and it is gratifying to see that they are already producing a healthy revenue. These satellites serve as relays between powerful ground stations on different continents and are used as effective transoceanic links for telephone service and television programs. However, this is only a beginning. Within a few years, the leasing of transcontintal landlines for national U.S. television hookups will be a thing of the past, as communications satellites can render this service at a fraction of the cost. Another, even more exciting thing will be a TV broadcasting satellite in a synchronous orbit—a station seemingly standing still in the sky, to which anyone on the earth below can tune his private receiver. Several hundred kilowatts of orbital transmitting power would be required. The social and political implications of such a system are enormous. David Sarnoff, Chairman of the Radio Corporation of America, said in a recent speech that with such a satellite, illiteracy could be eradicated from the face of the earth within ten years.

Would such a TV broadcasting station be manned? It may well prove to be economical to furnish a station so complex and powerful with a permanent maintenance crew, which would be exchanged at periodic intervals.

A deep-space assembly site and jump-off platform for manned expeditions setting out to land on other planets. Such missions will require nuclear-powered spaceships assembled and fueled in a low earth orbit from sections and propellants brought up by chemical earth-to-orbit freighters.

A major problem is affecting the design of manned space stations. It is raised by the possible ill effects from a long period of weightlessness.

Early space-station designs called for doughnut- or dumbbell-shaped stations rotating slowly about their hubs so that centrifugal force would replace at least a part of the missing gravity. But a spinning platform would handicap obervers of the heavens and the earth, since telescopes require a steady aim. The same applies to large directional antenna dishes.

We still do not know whether, for space station crews serving hitches of several months, artificial gravity will be necessary from the medical point of view—and, if so, whether a daily five-minute spin in a small centrifuge built into a nonrotating space station might not suffice to make both the astronaut and the doctor happy. In any case, artificial gravity undoubtedly would add to the comfort of everyday life in a space station.

Space stations may differ in design according to their respective purposes. Likewise, their uses may dictate orbits of widely different types.

Unless the mission specifically calls for a high orbit, a low one offers the general advantage of lower earth-to-orbit transportation cost. A low west-east orbit, only slightly inclined to the equatorial plane, is particularly economical: It gives a rocket ship, at launching, full advantage of the "boost" resulting from the earth's west-east rotation. Such an orbit would best suit a space station intended as an astronomical observatory—or as a physical and life-science laboratory. A relatively low polar or near-polar orbit, in contrast, seems advantageous for earth surveillance, since it would enable an observer to see every point on earth at least twice in twenty-four hours.

For an assembly site for deep-space expeditions, a low orbit in the equatorial plane offers certain advantages. And a TV station "fixed" in space automatically calls for an equatorial orbit, with the added requirement of a twenty-four-hour orbital period (which, in turn, sets the required orbital height at about 23,000 miles).

To sum up, manned space stations are bound to come. Because of their varied potential uses, and different requirements, it seems likely that we shall have not one but a number of space stations—and that, in due time, other countries will have theirs, too.

It may well be, however, that several mission assignments for future manned space stations can be combined and served by one central station, when all participants can agree on an identical orbit. To reconcile the missions' different needs as to design, the orbiting space center may consist of a group of small free-floating "mission" stations, clustered about a spinning doughnut or dumbbell that will serve as a combination hotel, restaurant, and office for the entire complex.

Observatories in Space

Radiation from stars, nebulae, and distant galaxies provides the only clue to our understanding of the extraterrestrial world. Space vehicles can be used to study this world more thoroughly than this could ever be done from the earth's surface.

Outer space is pervaded by the entire spectrum of electromagnetic radiation, shown in my diagram. It ranges in wave length all the way from 0.00003 Angstrom (an Angstrom is one ten-billionth of a meter) up to 3,000 meters. The corresponding frequencies also are shown in the diagram.

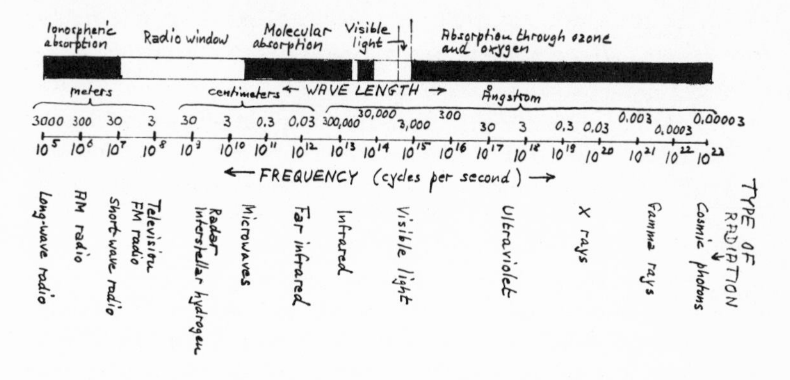

The spectrum of electromagnetic radiation.

But we live at the bottom of a dense atmosphere that absorbs most of this radiation, and so is opaque to it. Only a small portion penetrates to the earth's surface. In essence, our atmospheric shell provides only two "windows": one for visible light (with wave lengths of 4,000 to 8,000 Angstroms) and a bit of the infrared, and the other for radio waves (between about 1 centimeter and 30 meters in wave length).

For centuries, astronomical observations of celestial objects were limited to the narrow window admitting visible light. In recent years, radio telescopes have opened the "radio window" and gleaned much new information.

Space vehicles, operating outside the earth's atmosphere, can observe the *entire* spectrum of electromagnetic radiation. Manned or unmanned, they offer an ideal platform for studying the universe, with radiation-sensitive instruments that cannot be used on earth. Even a casual glance at the little diagram shows that these new observational tools are bound to multiply our knowledge of the universe.

We expect plenty of practical use from the study of the universe of which our own planet is such a tiny part. Nothing is more difficult to predict than the profitable applications of a new discovery. But in the last analysis, all the things that fill our everyday needs—the food we eat, the clothes we wear, the automobiles we drive—are the result of someone's desire to explore the unknown.

The harnessing of nuclear power, whether in the atom bomb or in a power-generating reactor, can be traced back directly to astrophysical studies—of the sun, in particular.

We should always bear in mind that all plant and animal life on earth would be extinct within a few hours if the sun suddenly ceased to shine. It is clear that a better understanding of the mechanism of energy transfer from the sun to the earth will lead to a better understanding of everyday problems down here on earth.

Although the sun seems never to change in appearance, it is actually subject to erratic behavior. Its surface may be perfectly clean today; a month later it may be covered with dark spots. Sunspots are an indication of activity that bears some resemblance to volcanic eruptions on earth. The difference between the two phenomena is that the gas expelled by the sun—predominantly hydrogen—is so hot that the hydrogen atom (consisting of a proton and an orbital electron) is deprived of its electron. As a result, the solar gasburst, or flare, consists of protons or electrons.

Under "quiet" conditions, there is a more-or-less steady flow of these particles, called "solar wind." This flow travels all the way from the sun to the earth and beyond. During average solar eruptions the density of this flow increases a hundred-fold or more, and the velocity at which the particles reach the earth is also markedly higher. Once a year or so the eruption of a gigantic flare is observed, with particle densities and speeds far exceeding those in normal flares.

For manned space flight, only these giant flares are considered hazardous. A program to predict such flares has been initiated, and it is planned to time short trips (such as round trips to the moon) so that they won't coincide with the superflares. On long interplanetary space voyages it may be necessary to take along "storm cellars" into which the crews could withdraw during the hours of peak intensity of the flare.

The sun is our most powerful source of stellar radiation. We can consider it the nearest fixed star. Because of the window problem, we still know very little about solar ultraviolet and X-ray radiation. But what little we have learned so far from artificial satellites clearly indicates that some of the previous ideas held by astrophysicists—particularly about the intensity of ultraviolet emissions of hot stars—have been woefully wrong.

We are still completely in the dark about the causes of the sun's mysterious eleven-year sunspot cycle. Scientists have known for years that there is a close correlation between this sunspot cycle and the earth's magnetic variations and polar lights. The discovery of the Van Allen Belt has provided some clues for the mechanism of this interaction. But we simply do not know what causes the sun to "breathe" in that cycle.

Conceivably, part of the heat energy continuously released by the huge thermonuclear reactor operating in the sun's interior, instead of flowing evenly outward to the surface, may be dammed up in some fashion so that it comes through in rather gentle periodic surges.

Variable stars with great changes in brightness are quite common in the universe—and it is fortunate indeed that our own sun's cyclic variations are so small that a hundred years ago it was not even known they existed. They went undetected for so long primarily because the sunspot cycle is not accompanied by any noticeable variation in visual brightness—in other words, as observed by visible light.

In the previously inaccessible ultraviolet region, very noticeable fluctuations have been recorded.

NASA's new orbiting solar observatories are equipped to record such radiation data. But for broad conclusions we must be a bit patient. We'll have to wait for the length of at least one eleven-year cycle.

There is a definite connection between the sunspot cycle and the weather. Meteorologists have learned, to their dismay, that the statistical accuracy of their predictions is adversely affected by increased ultraviolet radiation from the sun.

The reason for this is easy to understand: The classical method of weather forecasting has been based upon the principle of causality. In other words, the U. S. weather map for Tuesday is a direct, logical deduction from the trends depicted on the weather map for Monday. But such cause-and-effect reasoning is permissible only as long as one analyzes a "closed system," such as an atmosphere subjected solely to internal disturbances, while exposed to a steady, predictable influx of solar radiation. As soon as the situation is altered by external factors—such as unrecognized changes in solar ultraviolet radiation—the beautiful causal reasoning falls apart, and the results of weather predictions become disappointing.

While a lot of sporadic data have been collected, there is no operational, round-the-clock, satellite-borne recording system for solar ultraviolet radiation in existence today. But within a few years we shall have it. Along with making a continuous survey of the atmosphere's ozone layer (which goes up to sixty-mile altitude and can be reached with simple rocket probes), it will enable meteorologists to pin down exactly those external influences on our weather. Tiros and Nimbus-type satellites, with their TV cameras and infrared sensors, will keep a watchful eye, day and night, on the earth's ever-changing cloud patterns, too.

Once all these new sources of knowledge are tied in with the existing weather stations, by a rapid-fire global communications system, we can rightfully expect weather forecasting to reach new heights of accuracy.

Observatories in space are ideally suited for the study of yet another phenomenon that is of great interest both for cosmologists and designers of space vehicles: cosmic radiation. The term cosmic radiation, or cosmic rays, is used for elementary particles that crisscross outer space at velocities approaching the speed of light.

The majority of these particles are protons, the nuclei of atoms of hydrogen (atomic weight, 1). But heavier nuclei up to those of indium (atomic weight, 114.8) have been detected. By and large, the particle count diminishes with increasing particle weight, but some heavier elements such as iron (atomic weight, 55.8) are relatively abundant. Although evidence is still a bit sketchy, some scientists believe that the atomic-weight distribution of cosmic rays reflects the relative abundance of the chemical elements throughout the universe.

This has led to the theory that cosmic rays might be the debris of tremendous thermonuclear explosions of stars. Such exploding stars have been observed by astronomers and are called *supernovae*.

However, some cosmic-ray particles travel so fast that even a supernova explosion could not account for their energy. It is believed such high-energy particles derive their extra speed from being bounced back and forth, between the magnetic fields that accompany vast, moving interstellar clouds of extremely tenuous ionized gas or *plasma.*

Cosmic radiation of a lesser energy level is known to come from the sun, particularly during solar flares. Such lower-energy particles approaching the earth are deflected, by the earth's magnetic field, toward the North and South Poles. Thus, total cosmic-ray intensity is at a minimum over the earth's equator.

Cosmic-ray particles as encountered in outer space are often called *primaries,* to distinguish them from the cascade of secondary particles generated by their collision with air nuclei in the upper layers of our atmospheric shell. These secondary particles shower down through the atmosphere. Although their intensity tapers off with decreasing altitude, they can be detected at the ground and even several hundred feet under water.

The question of the long-time physiological hazards of cosmic radiation to astronauts is still hotly debated. Surprisingly, radiologists are not concerned about the most energetic primary particles. These go through the human body so fast that they have no time to do damage.

The greatest potential hazard is posed by a slow, heavy primary that comes to a "screeching halt" in the human body. In this case the positively charged primary particle has time enough to jerk a whole string of electrons out of the atomic shells of the body tissue, along the path of its "terminal retardation" or final braking. Some radiologists believe that certain areas of the human body, such as the brain and spinal cord, might be endangered by extensive exposure to such "slow-down hits." Hence, they are advocating extra radiation protection for longer space flights.

Now It's Time to Put a Living Room in Orbit

"Inject water, knead, and squeeze the broth through your teeth." Day after day of such Spartan fare for food, and of all the other hardships of their Gemini 7's cramped quarters, tested the fortitude of Frank Borman and Jim Lovell in their record two-week space flight in December, 1965.

Pioneering has always been uncomfortable. No band of men could ever have been more willing to accept its discomforts than our astronauts. But coming missions will demand making manned spacecraft more livable.

Our manned-space-flight program is entering its second major phase. Now that we have demonstrated that man can live and work in space for a long time, we must put man to practical use. And future manned space missions should be the more useful, the longer man stays out there.

For a long time to come, space flights will be expensive. The costliest single item, until we have re-usable launch vehicles, will be the rocket booster. Thus, the more useful time we can get out of a single launch, the less will be the cost per man-hour in space.

A miles-to-the-gallon approach favors long missions, too. Each manned launch into orbit costs many thousands of gallons of fuel. But once the crew is up there, no more fuel is needed to keep them there. With each circuit in low orbit they travel about 27,000 miles. Thus, if a manned spacecraft stays up for enough orbits, its economy can put a Volkswagen to shame.

Long stay-times in orbit will therefore be the rule, rather than the exception, for useful manned missions near the earth. For a man to work long and most proficiently in space, we must provide him with a reasonable degree of comfort—whether he serves as a pilot, scientist, repairman, operator of commercial equipment, or military observer. And this is just as important for future astronauts setting out for the planet Mars, a voyage that may last well over a year.

The basic ingredients of comfort in space flight are not too different from our ideas of comfort on earth:

Temperature. When there is not much physical activity, 72 degrees F. is considered ideal. Variations should not exceed five degrees warmer or cooler. Environmental-control systems of spacecraft can easily maintain the temperature within this range, however long the stay in space.

Atmosphere. Present-day U.S. spacecraft provide a pure-oxygen atmosphere to breathe at the low pressure of a little less than five pounds per square inch (absolute). This is about one-third of the normal atmospheric pressure (14.9 pounds per square inch), and is like that atop Mount Everest. But a breath of pure oxygen at five-pound pressure gives the lungs enough—more oxygen, in fact, than is in a breath of three-times-denser normal air (21 percent oxygen, 79 percent nitrogen).

The low pressure, besides saving spacecraft weight, gives space suits maximum flexibility to make wearers' movements easy. Using the same pressure in spacecraft cabins and space suits avoids complications in changing from one to the other—for a space walk or in case a sudden failure of the cabin's pressure system forces the astronauts to close their helmets' faceplates and depend on the life-giving atmosphere in their suits.

As to how long astronauts can breathe pure oxygen without harm, however, there is considerable argument. The Gemini 7 flight proved that two weeks is acceptable. But how about a year? No one really knows. Chances are that for lack of experience spacecraft or space stations designed for operating periods such as a year will go back to good old air—just to play it safe.

Privacy. Many of us value the right to be left alone. After a year in space in crowded quarters even the way the other guy eats, clears his throat, or tells a joke for the umptieth time can be trying.

Ground stations want continuous contact with an orbiting spacecraft, as with an airliner—and radio chatter is no lullaby to a man trying to sleep three feet away in a spacecraft. "Noise separation" for more privacy will be needed in the future. So will "light separation." Many cannot sleep with lights on. Today's astronauts may have no such problem, but some astronaut-scientists of the future undoubtedly will. Private quarters for the sleeping shift thus become a must.

A man wants to wash, shave, and attend to his other bodily functions in private—another reason for more generosity in the assignment of floor space in outer space.

Food. Dehydrated and powdered food—reconstituted by moistening, kneading, and squeezing—may be fine for heroic explorers. But I think a man expected to perform at top proficiency in space for a year or more should get the same filet-mignon treatment as a business traveler on a supersonic flight from New York to Los Angeles.

Entertainment. We all need diversion. A man cooped up in a space station or interplanetary craft will want something to listen to, or look at—whether it is the Beatles or Beethoven, *Playboy* or Plutarch. Advanced techniques offer ways to keep our space explorers happy and balanced: taped music, microfilm libraries, laser for interplanetary color television.

Medical care. For a two-week trip to the moon and back an astronaut need only check in with his flight surgeon for a prompt okay. But that will not suffice for a one-year stay in orbit, or a trip of years' duration to a planet. Anyone can have a toothache or catch a serious disease a few months after his doctor found him in perfect health. So it stands to reason that long stays in outer space will require a physician at hand—and astronaut-doctors will become a part of the space-faring community, just as astronaut-astronomers and astronaut-meteorologists will.

Gravity. Borman and Lovell were perfectly happy after two weeks of zero gravity. Their comments sounded almost as if their major concern was whether they would ever again get used to the nuisance of earth gravity—which makes you toss about in bed to find a restful position, while in space you could fall asleep and awaken hours later without having moved one bit. But medical men still do not know what a year of zero gravity will do to a man.

In case all he needs is physical activity, it can easily be provided; by devices like rowing machines or spring exercisers.

If it does turn out that long exposure to zero gravity has detrimental effects—maybe a body centrifuge suffices to straighten things out again. Operated by electric power, or by pedal power supplied by the astronaut himself, it will obviate having to spin the entire craft to replace gravity with centrifugal force.

We shall have no problem in providing room enough for all these possible needs of extended space missions.

Saturn launch vehicles, designed to boost Apollo spacecraft to the moon, have huge liquid-hydrogen tanks in their upper stages. These tanks are empty on arrival in orbit. After being vented to the vacuum of space, they are clean as a whistle, free of odors other propellants would leave, and pressure-tight. They may then be filled with an atmosphere of pure oxygen or of any desired oxygen-nitrogen or oxygen-helium mixture. They provide ample room for a spaceman to "pitch his tent" in complete privacy—and can accommodate a kitchen, a doctor's dispensary, a shower bath, a men's room, a library, or anything else an astronaut on a one-year stint could desire. In a trial under NASA study that would make a spent 21-foot-diameter Saturn S-IVB stage habitable for thirty days or more, an Apollo spacecraft would dock with it, using a module providing a connecting airlock and an oxygen supply for the stage's interior. (The Saturn S-IVB stage serves as the second stage of a Saturn IB rocket for earth-orbit missions, and as the third stage of a Saturn V moon rocket for lunar injection.)

I think it is fair to say that the time has come when we are ready to break down the comfort barrier in space.

Space Tools

Future repairs, maintenance, and assembly work in space will require tools designed for unearthly working conditions. They must work reliably in a vacuum and at extremes of temperature. They must be usable by a man encumbered with a space suit and pressurized gloves—and must enable him to tighten a nut or saw a piece of spacecraft skin without putting himself into a tailspin. Despite these stiff requirements, space tools must be extremely light.

The problem of reliability, or rather the lack of it, of a complex spacecraft's many small parts has plagued our space program from its beginning. With the advent of manned space flight, the possibility was considered of giving astronauts a limited capability for maintenance of a spacecraft.

If a part failed, went the reasoning, why not replace it with a spare? It sounded attractive until engineers, eyeing details, ran into snags. How many tools does it take to change a fair number of parts? How does an astronaut check a repaired pressure line for leaks, or make sure a subsystem with a replaced part will work properly short of turning it on? Difficulties like these led to a sweeping but well-founded policy decision for the entire U.S. manned space-flight program: "There will be no inflight maintenance."

Yet, as missions grew longer and more complex, the desire to perform simple repair jobs, at least, was bound to reawaken. If something got bent in docking too fast, or if a hatch to scientific gear wouldn't open after a successful but rough lunar landing, an astronaut would want to get out a tool kit and do something about it. Like changing a flat on a car, this sort of thing was not really a maintenance task.

And so NASA now has a tool kit for astronauts after all. Developed for the Manned Spacecraft Center by the Martin Company, in cooperation with the tool firm of Black & Decker, the Space Tool Kit forms a completely integrated package fourteen inches long, fourteen inches wide, and ten inches high. Its metal shell has a rigid foam liner in which pockets have been cut to hold the tools and accessories.

Its centerpiece is a multipurpose power tool with a pistol grip. Interchangeable attachments convert the tool into an impact wrench, drill, or metal saw. A five-pound, 12-volt rechargeable battery, built into the toolbox, serves as the DC power source.

The innards of this deceptively simple-looking tool meet exacting requirements. Since there can be no air-cooling in the vacuum of space, the tool must absorb and radiate its heat. Ordinary lubricants would evaporate rapidly, especially from warm surfaces; silicone grease is the answer. Metal surfaces tend to cold-weld when forced together in the absence of oxygen; the saw design avoids this. Though heating conditions vary greatly in sunlight and shade, the pistol grip remains at a temperature compatible with the glove that grips it during extended use of the tool.

The astronaut himself poses even greater problems than does the environment. When he turns a nut with an ordinary wrench, an equal turning force or torque acts upon him in the opposite direction. If he were under zero gravity and without a firm foothold, the nut probably would not budge at all—and he would succeed only in spinning himself the other way around.

A wrench for use under zero gravity (as in orbit) or under low gravity (like the 1/6 G on the moon's surface) must eliminate or minimize this reactive force. It will do so if it can be squeezed instead of turned, but its tightening force will then be limited by the strength of the astronaut's grip. A power tool, to avoid reactive torque, must have a "closed force path" like that of a squeeze wrench.

Through a clever mechanism, patented by Black & Decker, the Space Tool Kit's impact wrench provides such a closed path. The electric motor twists and releases a spring about 3,000 times a minute. Hammer lugs, spun by this spring, impact sharply against anvils to turn a friction-braked output shaft. Thus a completely reaction-free pulse of torque is available to tighten that loose nut. The pulses exceed by many times the steady torque that either the astronaut's muscle power or the motor in the tool would be able to apply.

Even with a reaction-free tool, a man floating freely in front of his work under zero gravity would not be very effective. Therefore the Space Tool Kit includes a restraint system. Disks about an inch

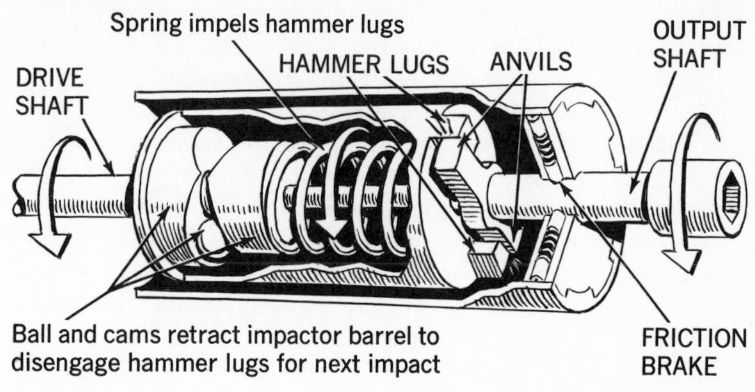

in diameter, glued to the outside of a spacecraft in flight, provide anchors for wires to tether an astronaut. Three wires will hold him firmly; in some cases two or even one will suffice. On the moon, he will not need to anchor himself at all.

Since Band-Aid-type of adhesive would not do under the extreme conditions of outer space, each restraint "button" has an epoxy surface, with electric heating wires embedded in it. Heating the epoxy bonding agent for about thirty seconds, while pressing the button against the spacecraft's skin, establishes a firm anchor point that will sustain a pull of up to about fifty pounds.

In space, lack of a light-scattering atmosphere results in extremely harsh contrasts between light and shadow. Working inside dark areas of the spacecraft, accessible only from the outside, is impossible without artificial lighting. After experiments with sunlight-reflecting mirrors and lamps attached to wrist or body, the most satisfactory solution has proved to be mounting lamps on each side of the astronaut's helmet—a variation on the idea of a miner's headlamp. Helmet lamps are therefore included in the Space Tool Kit.

A problem of major concern was eliminating the hazard of explosion and fire when the kit was used in the crew compartment of a spacecraft—which is filled at low pressure, five pounds per square inch absolute, with pure oxygen. Extensive test runs in this atmosphere finally led to arc-free electric-motor brushes and switches that couldn't spark a fire.

Other problems solved to everyone's satisfaction included restraining loose parts, like bolts, from floating away in zero gravity and adapting tools to be handled with the limited dexterity of pressurized spacesuit gloves. An "artificial fingernail," for a gloved finger, aids in manipulating small objects.

While the Space Tool Kit will serve for simple repair jobs, future manned missions will undoubtedly pose the task of assembling large structures in space. These may include big dishes for radio communication and radio astronomy and interplanetary space vehicles ferried up in sections by earth-to-orbit carrier rockets. Assembly jobs like this will require novel fabricating methods, particularly suited to use in space.

NASA's Marshall Space Flight Center has conducted an extensive survey of suitable techniques. Electron-beam welding, a new high-quality method requiring a high vacuum around the weld, proves extremely promising. So does cold welding, which applies the fact that metal surfaces, properly cleaned, will bond together even at room temperature in a high vacuum.

Another Marshall study involves electro-forming. When a high-energy electrical pulse surges through an electromagnet a piece of aluminum can be shaped by the impact of the strong magnetomotive force as if by a forging press. In outer space the electric energy can easily be collected with solar-cell batteries and stored in capacitor banks. Abruptly discharging these banks will yield strong electric pulses and magnetic fields, which can be put to good use in assembling large space structures. For example, the magnetomotive force created by a single discharge through a sleeve-shaped magnet, slipped over the telescoped ends of two sections of aluminum tubing, can join them inseparably.

All space tools and all assembly operations in space require advance studies and crew training in simulators. For realistic planning, questions that must be answered beforehand include the accessibility of operating stations, the time needed to complete a task in a full-pressure space suit, and the metabolic rate of the test subject while doing the job.

Tests in water-filled tanks with subjects using scuba-diving gear have helped to investigate problems of space-tool use under zero gravity. In experiments to study working on the moon, its low gravity is simulated by supporting five-sixths of a subject's weight with a fork-shaped arm, so that only one-sixth of his weight rests on his feet. As expected, it turns out that the force he can exert without losing his foothold is reduced to one-sixth of what he can apply when his feet support his whole weight under normal one-G gravity.

V. FLIGHT TO THE MOON

Do the Moon Photos Change Our Plans?

On July 31, 1964, at 6:25:49 A.M. Pacific Daylight Time, the Ranger 7 spacecraft impacted on the moon, about halfway between the Guericke and Lubiniezky craters, after radioing 4,316 pictures back to earth. So much did they tell that the hitherto nameless region where Ranger 7 crashed has since been named Mare Cognitum (Known Sea).

The pictures were taken with two wide-angle and four narrow-angle television cameras developed for NASA's Jet Propulsion Laboratory by the Radio Corporation of America. Picture-taking began eighteen minutes prior to impact, at an altitude of 1,300 miles, and ended with the destruction of the spacecraft on the lunar surface. The last picture was taken from 1,000-foot altitude and covered a 60-by-100-foot area. Its resolution was adequate to show objects on the lunar surface only 1½ feet across.

While it will probably take months or years to extract all scientific information of interest from the pictures, it is not too early to draw some important conclusions as to the feasibility of Project Apollo—NASA's program to land two Americans on the moon before the end of the decade.

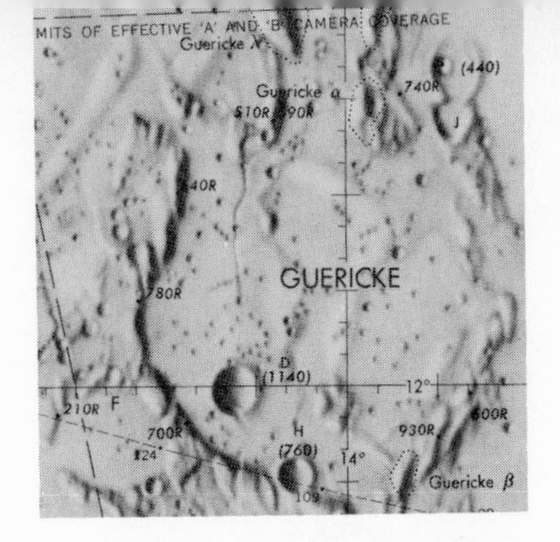

Air Force lunar map of Guericke based on the Ranger photo of the crater.

The pictures from Ranger 7 have given our confidence in a successful lunar landing a tremendous boost.

Certainly, the long flight of an Apollo spacecraft from earth to moon and back is fraught with all kinds of difficulties and hazards. Along with its Saturn V boost rocket, the spacecraft requires powerful and reliable rocket engines, a sophisticated structural design, complex trajectory calculations, and extremely precise guidance and navigation equipment. Success of the mission depends also on

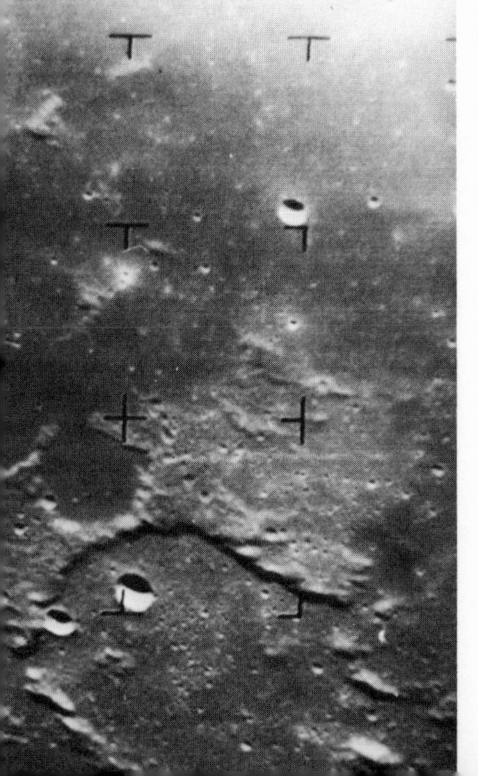

A Ranger photo of the crater Guericke from 470 miles away, which reveals detail ten times as small as on photos from earth.

training the astronauts in things ranging all the way from celestial mechanics and simulator runs to the art of cooking lizards as part of desert-survival techniques.

But there had always been one aspect of Project Apollo that had stubbornly defied all attempts at scientific investigation and better understanding:

What was the moon's surface really like? Was it covered with boulders and debris that would make a touchdown on the spidery landing legs of the Lunar Module hazardous or impossible? Was the lunar surface covered with dust—and if so, how deeply? Would the surface have enough bearing strength to support the spacecraft's weight? Would it support an astronaut walking on it—or a vehicle running on it?

The answers were so elusive because the most powerful astronomical telescopes, hampered by the turbulence of the earth's atmosphere, could distinguish nothing smaller than a mile across on the lunar surface. They are elusive no longer because the best close-up pictures from Ranger 7 have improved this resolution by about 2,000 times.

The first appraisal of the pictures was conducted by Dr. Gerard P. Kuiper, eminent Dutch-born lunar and planetary astronomer of the University of Arizona, and Dr. Eugene Shoemaker, famous geologist of the Institute of Astro-Geology in Flagstaff (under contract to NASA to help evaluate lunar-surface exploration meth-

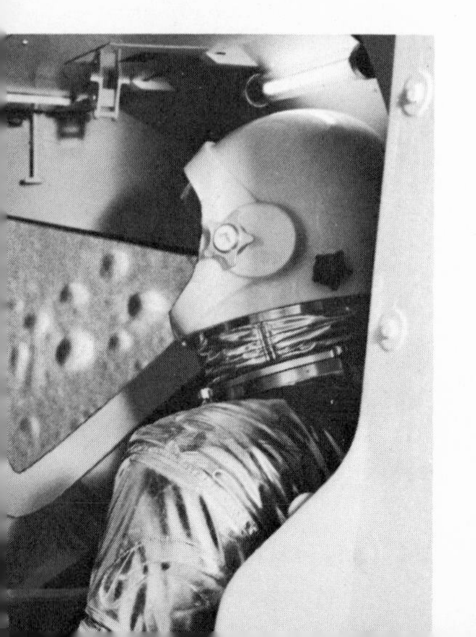

A landing-craft mock-up made by *Popular Science* with a Ranger photo of the moon taken from a 34-mile height inserted to show how the moon might look to an astronaut.

ods), whose main interest is the topography and structure of the lunar surface. Their findings can be summarized as follows:

> The Ranger 7 pictures show no evidence of deep layers of loose dust. On the contrary, the moon's surface looks to be pretty hard.
>
> The present design of the Lunar Module for the Apollo project is entirely adequate to land on terrain such as was impacted by Ranger 7. There is no need for any redesign of the Module or its landing gear.
>
> There is no need to abandon the old theory that lunar craters have been produced over millions of years by the impact of meteorites, ranging in size from a city block down to a grain of salt. This,

Disk-footed landing gear of Lunar Excursion Module is validated by the moon photos; its planned safe landing on the moon's rough surface at a tilt of up to 15 degrees from the vertical is shown to be adequate.

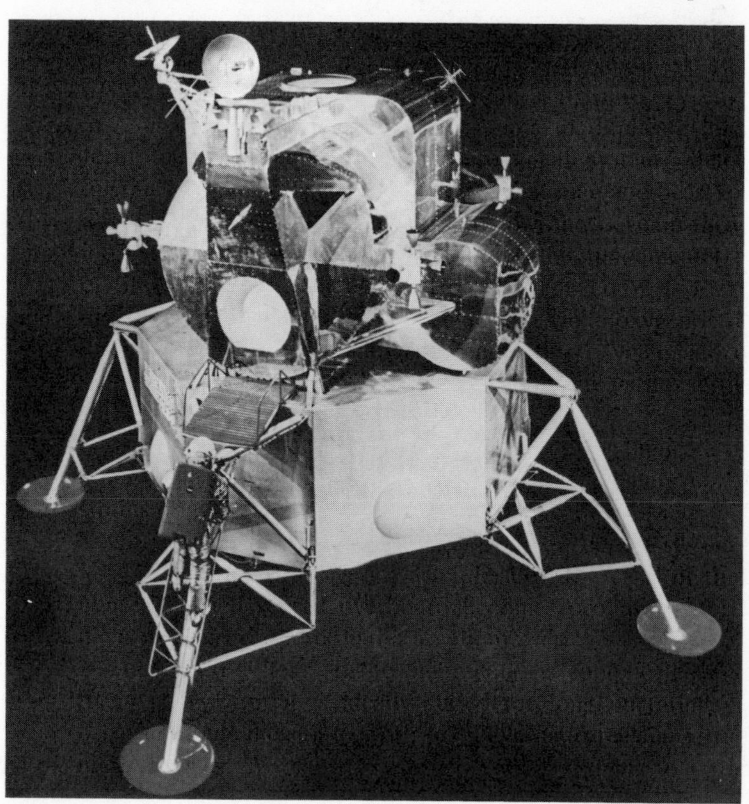

Photo taken by Lunar Orbiter 2 shows the trace of a boulder rolling down a slope. The boulder's print clearly proves the firmness of the lunar surface.

however, does not rule out the possibility of some limited volcanic activity on the moon which may have also produced some craters.

Ranger 7's pictures clearly show that the pattern of the tiny, hitherto invisible craters is not fundamentally different from the bigger ones. There are simply more of them. Observations on the statistical distribution of brighter and dimmer shooting stars in the earth's atmosphere are in full agreement with this finding.

Besides the craters and craterlets formed by "direct" hits, there are many "secondary" craters formed by rocks hurled away by meteorite impacts. The pictures indicate that these secondary craters tend to be grouped in clusters.

Black shadows in one secondary crater seen by Ranger 7 are cast by a large jagged rock that came to rest within the crater's rim—obvious proof that the bearing strength of the lunar surface must be considerable.

Conspicuous "rays" emanating from some of the "younger" craters such as Copernicus and Kepler are not, as had previously been surmised, made of some fluffy stuff. One older theory held that some powdery light-colored material had been tossed out of the moon's interior by the impacting meteorite. Another theory suggested that the rays were formed by volcanic gases, oozing out of the wound made by the meteorite, that subsequently froze in the cold lunar night on the darker ground beneath.

Drs. Kuiper and Shoemaker believe the Ranger pictures indicate that the rays should rather be looked upon as alleys of rocks and secondary craters along which most of the debris was hurled out by the impacting meteorite.

They conclude that the rays constitute rough areas particularly unsuited for safe landings. But even in a ray area, they feel, smooth landing sites big enough to accommodate a Lunar Module may be found.

Both Dr. Kuiper and Dr. Shoemaker, in discussing the Ranger 7 pictures' significance, repeatedly stated that scientists should not be expected to make any rash statements and evaluations in the face of a sudden windfall of unprecedented observations. Nevertheless, for all their guardedness, they saw fit to make the above statements without qualification. As an engineer, I can only add that on any terrain suitable for a touchdown by an Apollo LM, an astronaut can walk and a lunar surface vehicle can operate.

To some, Ranger 7's last pictures—though probably the most significant—may seem lacking in spectacular detail. If the moon is so dull-looking a place, is it really worth visiting? Of course the answer is that Ranger 7 was carefully aimed at an impact area in one of the dark, flat lunar plateaus (called mares because the ancients thought they were seas) that from the outset had been considered most suitable for a touchdown by the Lunar Module. Many other areas promise far more spectacular scenery or scientific mystery.

Less than 150 miles from where Ranger 7 fell is The Straight Wall—a tremendous cliff 60 miles long, more than 800 feet high, steeper than the Palisades of the Hudson River. There are mighty mountain ranges. There is the entire central area of the moon's southern hemisphere, virtually covered for some unknown reason with craters of all sizes—craters that overlap, even craters within craters.

Then there is the crater Kepler, center of a major ray system and one of the most conspicuous objects on the moon. Kepler and its walls and rays are undoubtedly one of the most rugged lunar areas, but one of the most intriguing research objects for a landing party. What pictures would another Ranger get if it were to descend into this crater, 22 miles in diameter and no less than 10,000 feet deep? What but another unmanned spacecraft can tell if a manned landing on the bottom is possible?

For the time being, however, Apollo must limit its ambitions and aims to less-difficult landing sites.

Our present appraisal of the lunar surface's nature and its suitability for a landing may be summarized this way:

The surface is made up of some porous, rocklike material—whose exact chemical composition is unknown and is even likely to vary between distant locations. Its porous nature results from incessant bombardment by tiny micrometeorites.

It appears likely that this hail of micrometeorites is even less dense on the moon than in a near-earth orbit, where we have no evidence that it ever endangered an astronaut or wrecked an unmanned spacecraft. However, the moon lacks a protective atmosphere like the earth's, and this bombardment has been going on for millions of years. This has created an extremely slow-acting, feature-changing force on the moon that might be called "meteorite erosion."

Whenever, every 10,000 years or so, a big meteorite throws up a big lunar crater—say, the size of our Meteor Crater in Arizona—the crater itself and the material splashed out look fresh for a while. The crater has a steep rim. A bright system of rays shows in which directions debris has been hurled. But the constant hail of small meteorites gradually erodes away the sharp features. Many old craters have no ray system. Some, in or near mares, look as if they were slowly filling up with dust.

Many people, including myself, have always held that there cannot be much loose dust on the moon—even though micrometeorites are incessantly kicking up some dust by splashing particles out of the rock they hit. A simple experiment shows that dust in a vacuum, as on the moon, becomes hard-packed. In fact, without any atmospheric oxygen around that could produce a contact-preventing oxide coating, "cold welding" of adjacent dust particles will fuse them together into a pumice-like substance.

The bearing strength of such a fused, porous material is hard to predict. Even Ranger 7 has not provided a complete and generally valid answer. Nevertheless, the qualities of snow offer a good illustration of what to expect:

Snow comes in various densities—from fresh-fallen "powder" snow, to the frozenover, melted-down snow called "firn." But all types of snow have in common the feature that, as you step on it, you sink in only until it is compressed enough to support your weight. While some powder snow may be too soft to walk on comfortably, all types of snow can at least be negotiated with skis or tracked vehicles.

There is reason to believe, however, that most of the moon's surface is substantially harder than soft powder snow. I think a

A model of a Lunar Orbiter which has scanned the moon. The globe at the craft's center holds a camera with lenses on the side pointed toward the moon.

man walking on a lunar mare will make a visible footprint and he may hear a crunchy noise (propagated to his ears through the artificial atmosphere in his space suit). But since his weight is reduced to one-sixth of his earth weight, he'll have no trouble walking.

Photo Spacecraft Circle the Moon

In June, 1966, the first of a series of five Lunar Orbiter camera spacecraft was launched. Circling the moon, it photographed extended belts of lunar terrain from surface-skimming orbits only twenty-eight miles high at nearest approach.

Taking pictures of potential landing sites on the moon for our Apollo astronauts is the main purpose of these unmanned, 850-

Course of a craft approaching and circling the moon—at first in high orbit, then in a low, moon-skimming one.

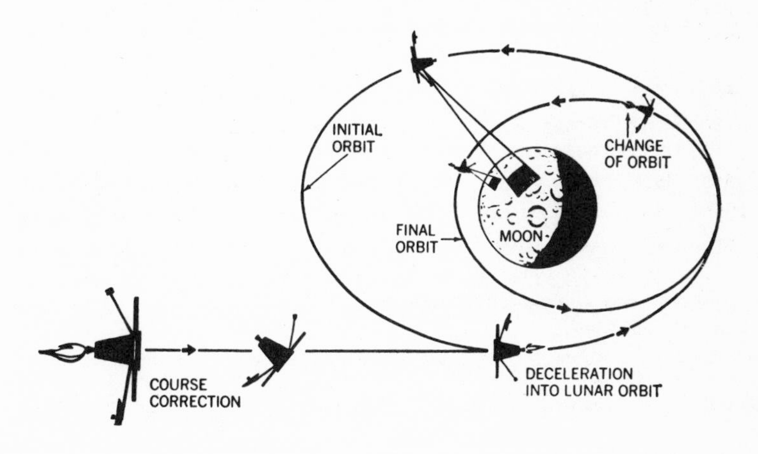

pound U.S. space vehicles. A secondary objective is to photograph larger areas of particular interest—on the moon's far side or in its polar regions—to gather a wealth of topographical and geological data.

What a Lunar Orbiter looks like may be seen from the model illustrated. A pumpkin-shaped container at the center houses the photographic equipment. Four black "paddles" are solar panels that generate 266 watts of electric power. The white arms extending from the sides are antennas—a dish-shaped directional one to bundle signals to earth after the spacecraft is properly oriented, and a fishing-reel-shaped antenna for continued radio contact between the craft and the earth during loss or temporary alteration of this attitude.

The nozzle atop the spacecraft model, protruding from a white heat shield, is part of the 100-pound-thrust rocket-propulsion system that enables the spacecraft to correct its course and to make changes in its lunar orbit.

Prior to Lunar Orbiter 1, the moon had been photographed by spacecraft maneuvered in three different ways: in a curving trajectory past the moon (Russia's Luna 3 and Zond 3), to a crash landing on the moon (our Rangers 7-9), and to a soft lunar landing (Russia's Luna 9 and our Surveyor 1). Photos from a moon-

Moon photographs by spacecraft

To date:			
1959	USSR	Luna 3	Far side, from about 40,000 miles
1964	USA	Ranger 7	Near side, up to impact (nearest: 1,000 feet)
1965	USSR	Zond 3	Far side, from about 7,000 miles
1965	USA	Ranger 8	Near side, up to impact
1965	USA	Ranger 9	Near side, up to impact
1966	USSR	Luna 9	Near side, on surface (after soft landing)
1966	USA	Surveyor 1	Near side, on surface (after soft landing)
1966	USA	Lunar Orbiter 1	
		(USSR's Luna 10, put in lunar orbit April, 1966, did not carry any photographic equipment)	
Coming, 1966-1967, USA:			
		Lunar Orbiter 2 to 5	Near and far sides, from about 28 miles
		Surveyor 2 to 10	Near side, on surface (after soft landing)

orbiting spacecraft are something new. Though not as close up as views from impacting or soft-landing spacecraft, they have the advantage of covering far more lunar territory at a range still near enough to disclose quite small details.

A Lunar Orbiter's single camera takes pictures alternately with a telephoto lens and a comparatively wide-angle lens. A frame made with the telephoto lens is able to register a 20-square-mile area so sharply that it is possible to distinguish an object as small as a card table. The wide-angle lens photographs about 350 square miles with high enough resolution to reveal a feature of the lunar surface no larger than a boxing ring.

Successive wide-angle frames overlap. A pair of the frames, like adjacent aerial photos of the earth, can be placed in a stereo viewer and seen in three dimensions—extremely helpful in relief, or contour, mapping. The ability to do this is another of the advantages of photographs from lunar orbit.

The film in a Lunar Orbiter's Camera is a long, 70-millimeter-wide strip. After exposure it passes through a processor in which it is developed and dried, yielding a high-quality film negative.

To transmit the pictures to earth, the TV-like technique is basically the same as the one successfully used in our Ranger spacecraft. A moving light beam scans the negative and falls upon a photomultiplier, which converts variations in lightness and darkness into corresponding fluctuations of electric current. This "electrical equivalent" is radioed to earth, where the process is reversed and a photographic image is reconstructed. Lunar Orbiter 1 ran into some difficulties with its optical equipment. The wide-angle lens pictures were perfect, but the pictures taken with the telephoto lens did not produce the high resolution expected because of a failure of the motion compensation feature. However, in the subsequent Lunar Orbiter 2 these shortcomings were corrected. In addition to perfect high resolution pictures Lunar Orbiter 2 radioed back some spectacular pictures of the Copernicus crater and the earth as seen from the moon.

A typical flight of Lunar Orbiter follows this program: An Atlas/Agena launch vehicle hurls the Lunar Orbiter from its pad at Cape Kennedy, Florida. The Agena, during its first burn after separating from the Atlas booster, puts the spacecraft into a parking orbit about a hundred miles above the earth.

A Ranger view covering 20 square miles of the moon's surface.

Then, at an instant determined by the moon's own orbital motion around the earth, the Agena restarts for its second burn. It pushes the spacecraft out of the parking orbit and into a moonbound course. On reaching a speed of about seven miles per second, the Agena shuts down, and the spacecraft separates from

This moon-surface photo was made by the USSR's space station Luna 9.

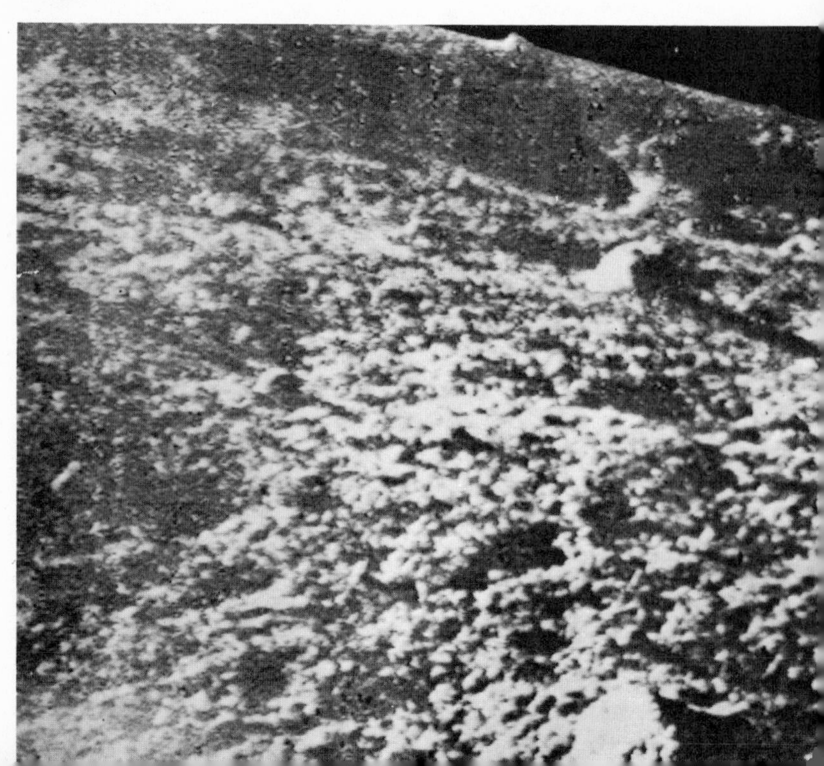

it—for a three-day unpowered coast to the moon.

During the journey, as well as afterward, nitrogen-gas jets control the attitude of the spacecraft so as to keep the directional antenna aimed toward the earth and the solar panels toward the sun. For this purpose, the jets are activated by a pair of sensors. A "sun sensor" keeps itself, and the lengthwise axis of the spacecraft, trained on the sun—the brightest object in the sky. Meanwhile a "Canopus star tracker," looking sideward, locks itself upon the brilliant star Canopus—thus checking rolling and completing the steadying of the craft in space.

When either the sun or Canopus is not visible, a gyroscopic "inertial reference unit" takes over attitude control of the spacecraft. During short passages through the shadow of the earth or moon, when the solar panels are inoperative, nickel-cadmium batteries provide electricity.

After a last correction of the spacecraft's course as it nears the moon, it brakes itself with its own rocket. This enables the tug of the moon's gravity to whirl it into a lunar orbit—initially, at a high altitude. (For awhile the course of Lunar Orbiter 1 was closely watched for "wobbling," due to any irregularities or departures

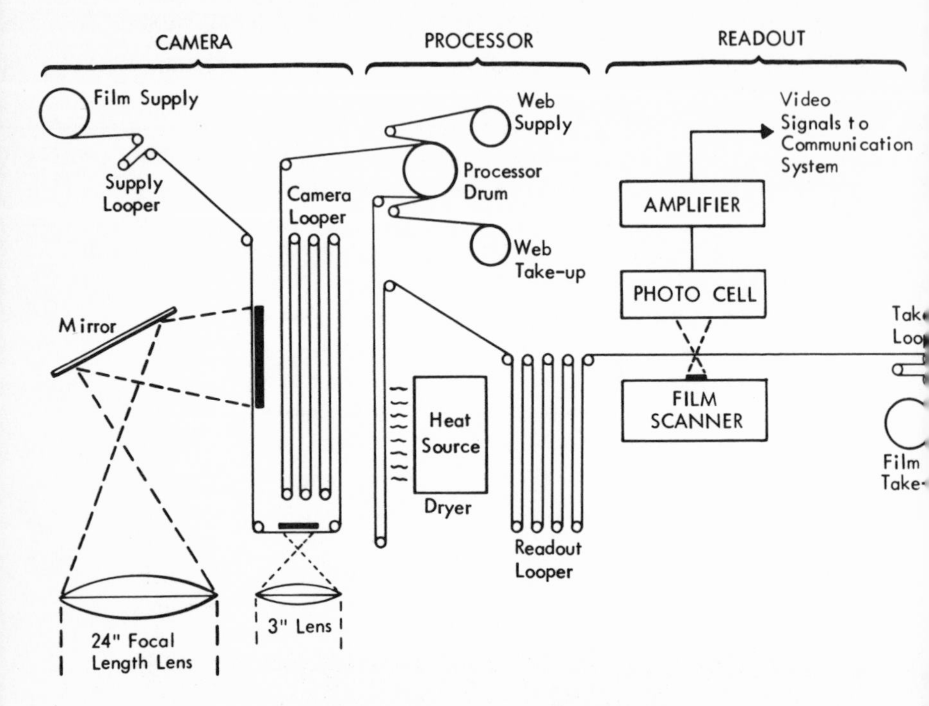

PHOTOGRAPHIC SUBSYSTEM

from symmetry in the moon's gravitational pull, to make sure it could safely be brought as near the surface as intended.) Then, by firing its rocket once more, the spacecraft changes its orbit to a low one that provides the best photographs.

After exposing all their film, the Lunar Orbiters transmit information for several months on the abundance of micrometeoroids and the level of radiation encountered in orbit around the moon. Gradual changes in the unpowered orbits will give scientists greatly improved data also on the moon's gravitational field and the lunar tidal effects produced by the earth's gravity. All this information is of vital interest to our forthcoming manned Apollo-Saturn flights to the moon.

Systems management of the Lunar Orbiter program is handled by NASA's Langley Research Center. The program's overall direction, on the Washington level, rests with NASA's Office of Space Science and Applications. Prime contractor is the Boeing Company, with Eastman Kodak and RCA the respective subcontractors for photographic and electronic subsystems. Evaluation of results is being co-ordinated by NASA-Langley, Jet Propulsion Lab, NASA-Houston, U.S. Geological Survey, Air Force Aeronautical Chart and Information Center, and the Army Map Service.

The Sea and Air Armada

An armada of ships and planes deployed around the globe will relay commands and flight data at critical moments of our Apollo astronauts' flight to the moon. The sea and air stations will complete a new communications network being set up for our three-man Apollo space flights, which now succeed our completed one-man Mercury and two-man Gemini series.

Manned space flights demand reliable radio links with earth to track the spacecraft's path, receive telemetered scientific and operational data, and provide voice communication for reports and commands between the astronauts and the Mission Control Center at Houston, Texas. So long as a spacecraft is within the line of sight of one of our land stations, scattered over the earth, they fill this need. But since water covers $7/10$ of the globe our Gemini program had to have three electronic support ships—the *Rose Knot Victor, Range Tracker,* and *Coastal Sentry Quebec.* Apollo flights will ultimately call for even more elaborate support.

The coming network will employ five newly converted tracking and communications vessels—the *Vanguard, Redstone, Mercury, Watertown,* and *Huntsville.* Two of these will support the first, earth-orbiting manned Apollo flight; all five, the lunar mission.

Each ship is the floating equivalent of a full-fledged land station. It provides tracking, telemetry, and voice communication with the astronauts. It will have two independent links to land: by a high-frequency voice circuit and via Comsat satellite. The ships have 12-knot speed and can stay at sea two months.

For the flight to the moon one ship will be placed in the Atlantic east of the Florida launch site to cover the tail end of the first phase—putting the Apollo spacecraft into a "parking orbit"

The communications ship *Vanguard,* converted from a T-2 tanker, begins its sea trials. Two of these antenna-studded ships will support early Apollo flights orbiting the earth; five will support the flight to the moon.

around the earth. Safe insertion in orbit and the needed orbital data will thus be reported to the Houston Control Center.

Two ships, one in the Indian Ocean and the other in the Pacific Ocean, will supplement land stations for tracking and other flight data at the critical time of the spacecraft's injection into its unpowered trajectory to the moon.

The remaining two ships, probably both in the Pacific, will provide tracking and communication during the spacecraft's re-entry into the earth's atmosphere. They may also be called in to retrieve the spacecraft and its crew upon splashdown in the sea—just west of Hawaii, according to present plans.

Eight communications aircraft, too, will aid the lunar flight. Converted from Air Force jet transports, they will be equipped not for tracking but for telemetry and voice communication. Thus the astronauts can talk with the crew of the plane or, by way of it, with the Houston Control Center. The planes have a top speed of 600 m.p.h. and, with a full fuel load, can stay aloft about twelve hours. A huge bulb at the nose, outwardly the most conspicuous addition for Apollo use, houses a seven-foot dish-shaped, sky-scanning antenna that locks onto the spacecraft for communications.

So elaborate a communications net is required for the lunar

An Apollo communications plane, one of eight, undergoes tests at Edwards Air Force Base in California. The bulbous protuberance at the nose contains sky-scanning antenna for voice and telemetry link with the spacecraft.

flight not because of the 238,000-mile distance to the moon but because of the moon's movement around the earth. If a space flight's objective is simply to orbit the earth we can take off whenever the launch crew is ready. But when we are to rendezvous with a target in space—whether it is an Agena or the moon—we have to time our launch in accordance with its position in orbit.

Thus, Gemini 11's successful rendezvous with an Agena in its first orbit required split-second timing of the Gemini's take-off from the Cape Kennedy launch pad.

The moon flight plan, instead, will allow a daily "launch window" of several hours' duration, and have the Saturn V's third stage stop over in a parking orbit where the space vehicle will get a final check before continuing the lunar voyage. The split-second timing is thus removed from the Cape launch pad and imposed on the instant of re-igniting the Saturn V's third stage, which will boost the spacecraft from earth orbit toward the moon.

The desired parking orbit is fixed in space. The earth rotates beneath it. So, as minor technical delays cause the moment of

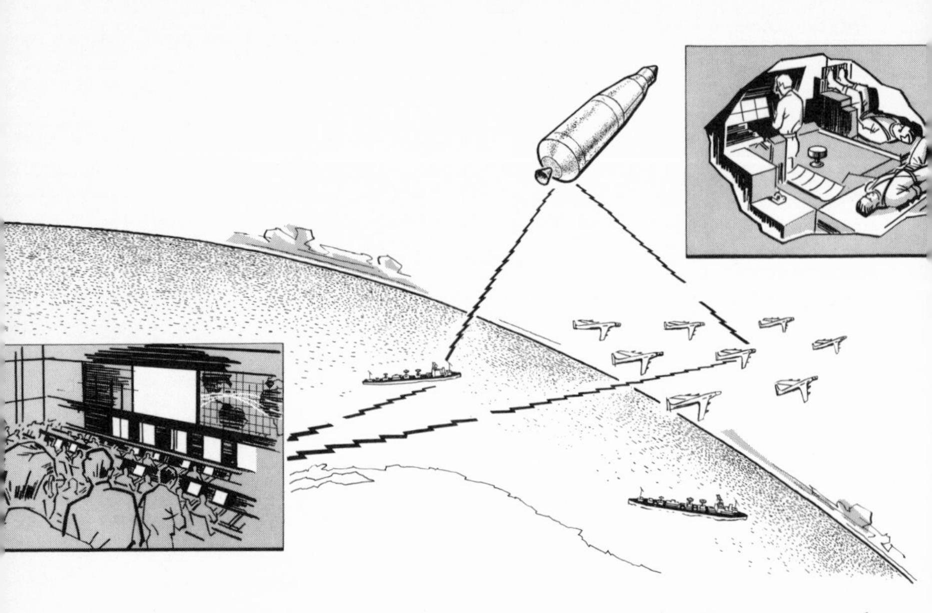

Ships and planes link Apollo astronauts with the Houston control center for the decision of whether to take off for the moon or not. The decision to "go" or "no go" must be made no more than 20 minutes after Saturn V's third stage boosts the spacecraft from the earth orbit into the course toward the moon—a critical moment of flight when the spacecraft may be out of sight and reach of the land stations.

launch from the Cape to slip, the launch azimuth of the Saturn V rocket must change continuously—say, from northeast to southeast between the beginning and end of a three-hour launch window. For the southeast heading, precision tracking by the land station at Antigua Island may be possible. But a northeast one may put the point of insertion into orbit less than 10 degrees above Antigua's horizon, too low for reliable data. Thus an "insertion" tracking ship is needed to protect the earlier launch option.

At injection into lunar trajectory the spacecraft's position must always be in the vicinity of the so-called lunar antipode: the point on the earth's surface where the extension of a rod connecting the moon with the center of the earth would come out at the opposite end. Due to the earth's rotation and the moon's own movement, this point can range far and wide over the globe. On any given day its exact location varies, depending on whether the Cape take-off

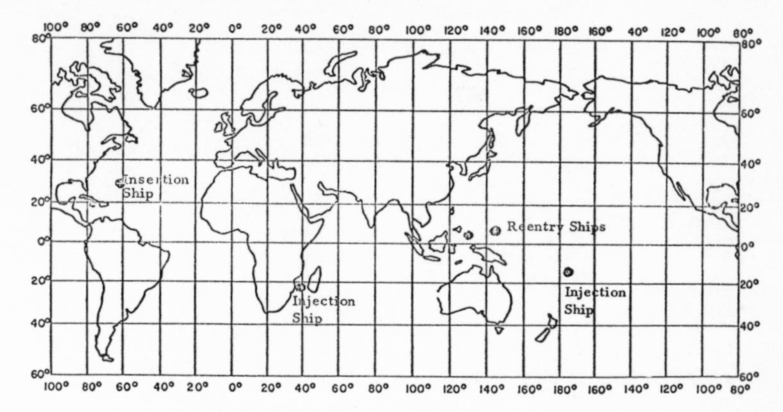

Typical ship support layout lunar mission

has been early or late in the launch window and on whether injection comes during the first, second, or third earth orbit. And, being governed by the position of the earth-orbiting moon, it will change with the launching date.

The Apollo planes will be mobile enough to chase the shifting point of injection and assure unbroken communication at this critical phase—the entire "burn" of the re-ignited third stage and the next twenty minutes of flight, in which must come the command decision to "go" for the moon or abort the mission.

For the re-entry from the moon, the Apollo sea-air net will be further augmented. If this maneuver cannot be conducted precisely as planned, the spacecraft may bounce back out of the atmosphere, before coming down once more at the end of a ballistic trajectory. In such an emergency case the astronauts possibly could miss their intended splashdown point by hundreds of miles. Precise tracking will be imperative to assure their prompt and safe recovery, particularly if splashdown occurs in an area of bad weather. Hence, a widespread fleet of forty-eight planes with advanced tracking gear will stand by to supplement the usual force of recovery aircraft. The tracking planes will locate the incoming capsule, follow it down, and render assistance wherever it lands.

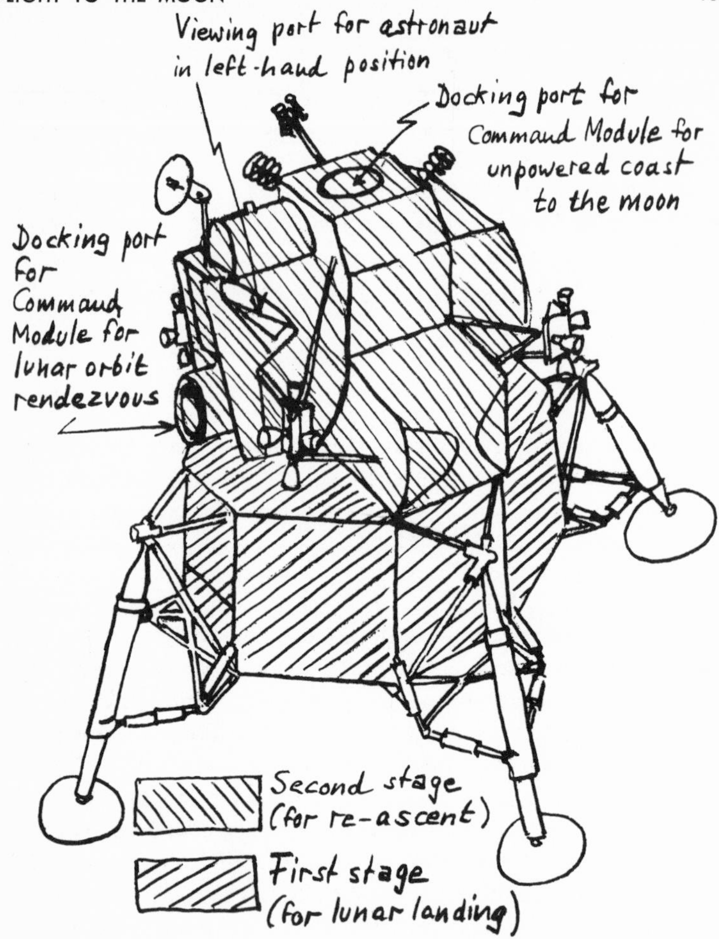

Astronauts Will Land on the Moon Standing Up

Astronauts will not sit in their spacecraft, but will stand suspended by straps when landing on the moon. This gives them better vision and more freedom of action, and it saves weight.

In Project Apollo, our national lunar-landing program, the actual touchdown on the moon will be performed with a separate vehicle called the Lunar Module, or LM. (See my sketch.) This two-stage, rocket-powered vehicle, with two astronauts aboard, will detach itself from its mother ship, the combined Command

and Service Module (CSM)—which remains in orbit around the moon with a third astronaut as "shipkeeper."

The LM slows down from initial circumlunar-orbit speed and touches down under the power of the throttleable rocket engine of its landing stage.

The return flight to the circumlunar orbit, and the rendezvous maneuver with the CSM, are performed with the second stage of the LM. This stage has its own rocket engine and propellant tanks, and uses the burned-out first stage as its launch platform on the moon.

The astronauts' compartment forms part of the second or upper stage—which, during the let-down maneuver, constitutes the payload for the first or landing stage.

In principle it would be possible, of course, to provide the urgently needed good vision for the two landing astronauts by fashioning the LM's crew compartment like the Plexiglas bubble cockpit of a small helicopter. However, such a solution would have a number of drawbacks.

For one, there is not room enough for a picture window. The flight deck of the LM is plastered with more instrumentation and displays than that of a large airliner. This is easy to understand. Not only must it provide flight control of two independent LM stages; the astronauts must also be able to perform quite a number of different tasks besides the critical maneuvers of touchdown on the lunar surface and rendezvous in lunar orbit with the CSM.

The astronauts must also be able to monitor their life-support systems continuously. Should the landing area prove unsuitable, they must be in a position to conduct a "landing abort" maneuver, with immediately ensuing return to lunar orbit and rendezvous with the CSM. They must communicate with the CSM and with the earth. They must be able to perform whatever navigation is necessary to correct for errors that may have made a rendezvous attempt unsuccessful at first try. The LM is equipped for all this and, in addition, has a complete inertial-guidance system of its own.

Then, too, a bubble-type compartment adds quite a bit of weight. For, unlike the cockpit of a helicopter, the LM must be pressurized.

Finally, for the touchdown on the lunar surface, the astronauts must have a good view down. They are interested in avoiding local obstacles, and they also would like to observe whether the surface of their selected landing spot has sufficient bearing strength to support the forward leg of their landing gear as it touches the ground. (If it doesn't, they can gun their landing engine and try to find a better spot nearby.) In addition to providing a good view downward, a window must offer a good view *upward* for the equally critical maneuver of rendezvous and docking with the CSM at the end of their landing excursion.

Another factor: The astronauts already are somewhat hampered in their freedom of action and field of view by their space suits and helmets.

All these considerations have led to adoption of a concept whereby the two LM astronauts will assume a standing position throughout all phases of the LM flight.

They will be supported by parachute-type harnesses attached to straps hung from the ceiling. This arrangement enables the astronauts to conveniently reach the many switches and view all the many dials within the LM crew compartment. Moreover, they can virtually press their noses against the relatively small windows, for a perfect wide-vision view outside.

Even for a helicopter landing on earth, there would be nothing wrong with a standing position for any of the crew members. In the LM, there is still less restriction upon choice of posture. The moon has only one-sixth of the earth's gravity—so, throughout the descent and ascent maneuvers, the accelerations within the LM will never exceed one g. In case of an exceedingly rough touchdown on the moon, a well-designed suspension system may even be safer than a conventional pilot's seat because of the longer travel available for the shock absorbers built into the suspension straps.

The resulting weight-saving is important, too. Every pound of LM, carried all the way to the lunar surface and back to the lunar-orbit rendezvous, is heavily mortgaged with more than 100 pounds of original departure weight from the earth's surface. The adoption of the "straphanger" concept substantially reduces the LM's weight by decreasing the size of windows for the pressurized cabin—and, of course, by omitting the heavy seats themselves.

Practicing a Moon Landing on Earth

Long before our first Apollo astronauts descend from a lunar orbit to the moon's surface, they will have practiced this critical maneuver on earth. They will get their training with a strange-looking flying machine called the Lunar Landing Research Vehicle, or LLRV, designed to simulate an Apollo landing on the moon.

Two of these craft were delivered in the spring of 1964 to NASA's Flight Research Center at Edwards Air Force Base, eighty miles north of Los Angeles and right in the heart of the Mojave Desert—a site resembling the moon's barren landscape. By late 1964 preliminary flight trials of the vehicles and their equipment were successfully concluded. Thereafter the LLRV's have begun fulfilling their purpose—to help engineers and astronauts familiarize themselves with the down-to-earth problems of putting a manned vehicle down on the moon.

Since an LLRV is to simulate a lunar landing, let us first examine the tasks it is to duplicate:

In Project Apollo, two of the three astronauts, while in orbit around the moon, will transfer from their capsule, or Command Module, to the Lunar Module, or LM. The LM in essence is a two-stage rocket craft. As it descends from lunar orbit under the power of its throttlable first-stage engine, the horizontal velocity is gradually reduced. At a few hundred feet above the moon surface, the LM is to hover motionless, while the astronauts select a suitable landing spot.

The touchdown maneuver itself resembles that of a helicopter, with the rocket engines' "thrust-control" lever replacing the chopper's "collective-pitch-control" lever. Shock-absorbing struts on the four legs of the spiderlike landing gear are to take care of the first contact, hopefully soft, with the lunar soil.

The return trip from the moon's surface to the orbiting Command Module uses the rocket power of the LM's second stage. The pressurized flight-crew compartment, which has served as the flight deck during the descent under the first-stage power, forms a part of the second stage.

The Lunar Landing Research Vehicle must do these things:

An LLRV maneuvers above the California desert during one of its preliminary trials.

Simulate as realistically as possible the terminal portion of the LM's descent from orbit–say, from 1,000-foot altitude and 40-m.p.h. horizontal speed down to contact with the lunar surface.

Allow for the moon's weak gravitational pull, only about 1/6 that of earth.

Take into account the moon's lack of an atmosphere.

Simulate the initial part of the ascent of the LM's second stage from the moon.

Permit simulation of an "aborted landing" on the moon. If the astronauts decided, a few seconds before touchdown, that the selected terrain did not look suitable for a safe landing attempt, plans would call for immediate return to the orbiting Command Module.

Provide maximum safety for trainees and vehicles. Specifically, have adequate redundancy so that no failure of a single part could cause a disastrous crash. Also, provide safe bail-out or ejection for the pilot, from all altitudes down to zero.

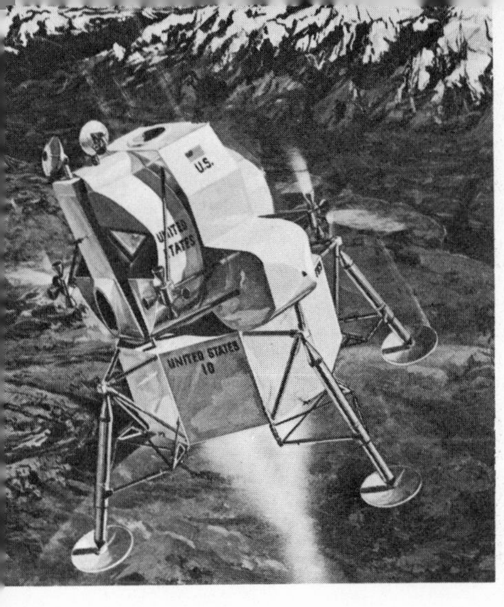

The descent of an LM to the moon's surface is simulated by the Lunar Landing Research Vehicle.

These are the specifications that the LLRV's maker, Bell Aerosystems Co. of Niagara Falls, New York, has sought to meet. The LM has often been called The Bug; the LLRV, which simulates its performance, could be called The Flying Bedstead.

Standing 10 feet tall, it has 4 truss-like legs spreading a little over 13 feet apart. With a full fuel load, it weighs in at about 3,000 pounds.

The open cockpit, a platform about six feet above the ground, extends forward from the main frame between the two front legs. It accommodates a single pilot. His equipment consists of an instrument panel, a side console, three control sticks (two for power, one for pitch-and-roll control), a pair of rudder pedals, an ejection seat, and an oxygen-breathing system to protect him from the thrusters' fumes.

The LLRV gets its lift principally from a vertically mounted General Electric CF 200-2V turbojet engine. This is actually a J85 jet engine with an aft fan attached, increasing its zero-speed thrust from 2,800 to 4,200 pounds. Mounted in a gimbal ring, the engine is gyroscopically kept pointed straight down, even when the craft tilts. To simulate a lunar landing, its thrust is throttled down to exactly five-sixths of the vehicle's weight.

The remaining one-sixth of the vehicle's weight is supported by two throttlable hydrogen-peroxide lift rockets of 500 pounds' maximum thrust each. They are mounted on the LLRV's main frame and tilt with the vehicle. Thus, they simulate the thrust of the LM's single throttlable descent engine. The turbojet engine simply cancels the excess of earth gravity over moon gravity.

Eight little rocket motors, likewise powered with hydrogen peroxide, control the attitude of the LLRV. Each attitude rocket is actuated by an individual solenoid valve of on-and-off type. As in a small plane, the pilot controls pitch by fore-and-aft movement and roll by right-and-left movement of a stick. Foot pedals provide yaw control. Stick and pedals are linked electrically to the solenoid valves.

In this fashion the LLRV duplicates the entire behavior of the LM—acceleration and attitude changes, and control response—under the true condition of one-sixth of earth gravity prevailing on the moon.

For a lunar-landing simulation, the LLRV climbs to desired altitude on the power of its turbojet engine alone, with gimbals locked in position. Then, with its nose pushed downward 10 degrees, it is accelerated forward by the horizontal component of the jet engine's lifting force. When the craft attains the desired conditions to begin a lunar-landing simulation—for instance, 1,000-foot altitude and 40-m.p.h. horizontal speed—the jet engine gimbal is unlocked to let its gyro stabilizer hold it "true vertical," and its thrust is throttled back to five-sixths of the craft's weight.

Since this weight changes as a result of fuel consumption, a simple computer tells the engine exactly what thrust is needed to equal five-sixths of the weight at any moment. Possible wind effects can be offset by a rather sophisticated steerage mode. Accelerometers pick up and identify any lateral or longitudinal acceleration that cannot be accounted for by the lift or attitude-control rockets—and that, therefore, must be caused by wind. In response, the gimbal actuators point the jet engine just enough away from straight down to compensate.

For safety, the LLRV has in reserve a standby set of six 500-pound-thrust lift-rocket engines, and a duplicate set of attitude-control rockets. It can fly with either set of each. A 22-foot drogue parachute will help in case of a jet-engine-out landing from a high altitude. As a last resort the pilot can eject—with a catapult-parachute system tested successfully even at ground level—or, given enough altitude, simply bail out.

An LLRV was first flown on October 30, 1964, by the late Joseph A. Walker, then chief research pilot of NASA's center at Edwards. Over the following year more than two dozen flights, averaging four to five minutes and reaching up to 800-foot altitude, served to check out the vehicle's performance.

With this preliminary phase completed, the LLRV's have now gone into service for practicing moon landings. At this writing, nearly two hundred simulated lunar descents have been made at the Edwards base. Two LLRV's will be transferred shortly to the Manned Spacecraft Center at Houston for use by the astronauts in training flights there.

What an Astronaut Will Wear on the Moon

Space suits, in which Apollo astronauts will walk the surface of the moon, have come a long way from the pressurized diving rig of rubberized canvas, topped by a cylindrical metal helmet, in which Wiley Post in 1934 attempted to break the world's altitude record.

The list of the Apollo suit's requirements is so long, and it is so conflicting, that for a long time some of the people closest to the problem expressed serious doubts whether the job could be done at all.

Just for a sample of the needs of a moon suit, it must:

Protect the wearer from the vacuum of space when the command module, or crew cabin, is depressurized—and when he is outside of it.

Keep the temperature around him comfortable, in all the following situations: inside the air-conditioned command module; outside the command module, both in bright sunlight and in the earth's shadow, during unpowered flight through space; and on the lunar surface, during day and night.

Provide a compatible backpack whose oxygen supply will last several hours—and can be renewed, by plugging in to the ship's oxygen supply, for periods up to several weeks.

Enable the wearer to eat and drink, under zero-gravity conditions, without breaking the suit's sealed atmosphere.

Permit him to communicate by voice when the command module

is pressurized and the three astronauts have their faceplates open; and by radio, outside the ship and on the moon's surface.

Give him a reasonable degree of protection from micrometeorites when he is walking on the lunar surface.

Permit storage and collection of body wastes, and have provisions for eliminating them.

Enable the wearer to walk comfortably over rugged terrain on the moon (where the gravity is only one-sixth of what it is on earth), with the suit pressurized and backpack in place.

Allow him to get back on his feet unaided, if he should stumble and land on his back like a June bug.

Permit him to do work requiring some manual dexterity, with his suit and gloves pressurized.

Be light and flexible—yet sturdy enough to avert critically dangerous punctures by contact with jagged rock formations on the moon.

Enable the Apollo astronaut to shed or don it quickly in the cramped space of his command module, under zero-gravity conditions and without help.

These dozen items' desirability will be as obvious as the difficulty of providing them. They have been likened to "a shopping list for Santa Claus."

The Apollo moon suit is the answer to this imposing array of specifications. It is being developed by the Hamilton Standard Division of United Aircraft at Windsor Locks, Connecticut, under a contract with NASA's Manned Spacecraft Center, Houston, Texas.

The forthcoming Apollo moon suit is best described by progressing, stepwise, from the astronaut's skin outward.

To remove body heat effectively, the innermost garment is a set of water-cooled long johns, worn directly on the bare skin.

Pictures of Mercury astronauts emerging sweat-drenched from their capsules have conveyed, in a rather telling way, the need of active cooling for a man hermetically sealed in a pressure suit. Oxygen circulated through the Mercury suit, before launch and during flight, was called upon to remove body heat. But water-circulating plastic tubes, embedded in a net-weave undergarment, have been found far more effective—and are therefore used in the Apollo suit.

The heat absorbed by the cooling tubes is dissipated in the

astronaut's backpack by a porous-plate "sublimator"—a novel sort of raditor for space conditions. Warmed water from the cooling tubes is sucked into pores of a plate whose other side is exposed to the ambient vacuum. The water freezes in the pores, due to pressure drop and evaporation.

As the resulting ice sublimes (evaporates without melting) into the vacuum outside, the "ice plug" in each pore grows thinner. Ultimately it blows out, the pore refills with water, and the cycle is repeated. Thus the porous plate serves as a stationary heat-rejection device.

A thin layer of nylon, whose texture and function can best be compared with those of a shirt, surrounds the water-cooled undergarment. This nylon layer also supports oxygen ducts, and wiring for medical instrumentation taped to the astronaut's body.

Next comes the sturdy "pressurization layer," a heavy bladder of neoprene-coated nylon. Its main function is to seal within the suit the astronaut's pure-oxygen atmosphere, which is at an absolute pressure of five pounds per square inch—about one-third of the atmospheric pressure on earth.

As could be expected, the design of easily movable joints at hips, knees, shoulders, and elbows posed a most formidable problem. For any flexible L-shaped joint, unless especially configured, has a natural tendency to straighten out under pressure. Of course, this would mean that an astronaut thus encased would have to use brute force (and plenty of it) to bend a knee or an elbow.

The answer to this dilemma is the "convoluted joint"—a rubberized bellows joint, so designed that its total internal volume does not change as it is deflected. A complex system of internal nylon and wire prevents the bellows from expanding like an overpressurized accordion.

Other vital elements tied to the pressurization layer are the pressure-glove and boot connectors, and the helmet ring. Pressure gloves and boots are attached to the suit with quick-connect O rings and bearing seals to prevent oxygen leakage. The fiberglass helmet of the Apollo suit can be rotated on the astronaut's shoulders, if he so chooses, as he turns his head.

An outer restraint layer of nylon, aluminized on the outside, encloses the pressurization layer.

On the lunar surface, the Apollo astronaut will don in addition a loosely fitting overgarment—a two-piece set of pants and cloak of aluminized mylar and nylon—a sort of "thermal overcoat." This will provide him with additional protection from the extremes of temperature between sunlit and shaded areas on the moon. It will also serve as a protective shield against grain-of-salt-sized micrometeorites, which are believed enough of a hazard on the lunar surface to warrant this extra protection. This thermal overcoat is contoured to fit over the life-support and communications backpack.

That is a preview of the way the Apollo astronauts will be dressed for the great adventure of setting foot upon the first of the celestial bodies to be explored by earthmen.

What We'll Do on the Moon

Our astronauts' first landing on the moon is now probably less than a thousand days away. What will they do when they get there?

Even the earliest and briefest missions will begin an exciting program of exploration to solve long-standing mysteries of the moon. This many-faceted program will later reach full swing when more-advanced spacecraft enable explorers to remain longer on the moon and to make extended journeys across its surface.

New details of what our first Apollo landing party will do, when the two astronauts have left their three-man mother ship in lunar orbit and set down their landing craft on the moon, have been made public by NASA.

From touchdown to lift-off they will remain on the moon for eighteen hours. Twice, both astronauts will emerge from a hatch of the Lunar Module, their landing craft, and venture together over the lunar surface—for three hours each time. The rest of their stay will be taken up in checkouts of their craft and life-support gear, communications, and a six-hour period for eating and sleeping between trips outside.

Collecting samples of moon rocks and soil to bring back for study will be a major activity of their six hours of exploring. They will take photographs of the lunar terrain, too, and inspect and measure the "footprints" of their own craft in the lunar soil. Finally, they will spread out on the lunar surface, a safe three hun-

The first astronauts to land on the moon will leave instrument packages, which will send data back to earth after they have gone.

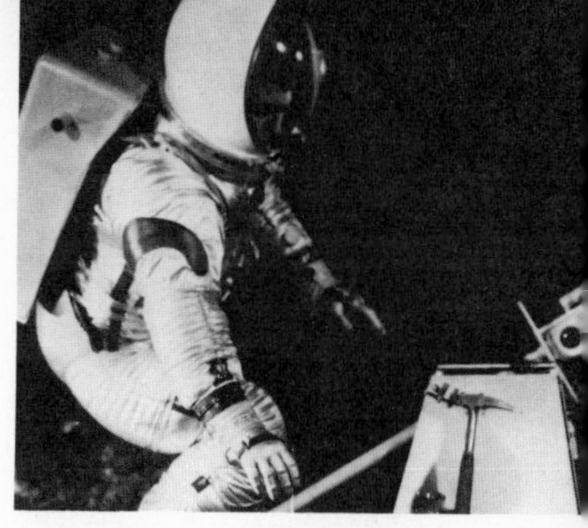

dred feet away from their point of takeoff, an array of scientific instruments that will automatically radio information back to earth for at least a year after they have left the moon.

A mock-up of this Apollo Lunar Scientific Experiment Package (ALSEP) was recently demonstrated at NASA's Manned Spacecraft Center in Houston. It includes a variety of instruments to observe the lunar-surface environment and others to probe beneath—by such means as a grenade launcher to produce artificial seismic waves and a seismometer to detect them. An atomic battery called SNAP-27, being developed especially for ALSEP, will be the 50-watt thermoelectric power source. The astronauts will insert its plutonium fuel capsule after landing on the moon.

From this modest beginning will unfold a vast project of lunar exploration designed to answer questions as varied as these:

Are there living organisms on the moon—perhaps completely different from any on earth? Microbiological experiments on lunar samples, from the surface and below, should tell. Likewise to be sought in the samples are primeval organic substances, like those from which life originated on earth, and oxygen and traces of water that might be extracted from lunar materials to help support future bases on the moon. Geologists will be eager to identify the lunar minerals themselves, and deduce the manner in which they were formed.

This mock-up shows how the instrument package will be spread out on the moon's surface. The black object at the far right represents the atomic battery.

Is there a trace of a lunar atmosphere and how much? Since it must be so tenuous that even Lunar Module rocket engines may contribute substantially to it, scientists urge beginning its study as near as possible to the start of the Apollo program.

What is happening in moon craters, like Alphonsus, that show signs of activity? These "thermally active" craters, the maria or "seas," and the cratered highlands will be the three main types of lunar terrain of interest to explorers.

How was the moon born? Was it torn from the molten earth by solar gravity or did it and the earth condense from the same rotating gas cloud, or were moon and earth both built up from solid fragments orbiting the sun in disarray—the "accretion" theory now favored? Investigating the moon's history figures largely in a list of fifteen key moon questions that the National Academy of Sciences, in close cooperation with NASA, has prepared. For this may well tell us more about the earth's own past. While our planet's birthmarks have been virtually eradicated by erosive forces like wind, rain, floods, and vegetation, those of the airless moon should be preserved.

Implements for answering such questions will include:

Long-handled scoops to gather loose rocks, simple scales to weigh their load, and containers to seal them in.

Drills to collect core samples and probes to measure temperatures in the outer 10 to 100 feet of the moon's crust.

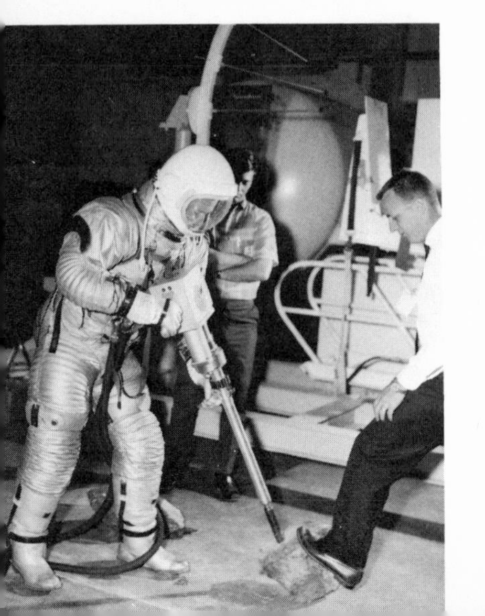

A prototype portable battery-powered core drill, used for cutting samples from solid rock on the moon's surface, getting a trial at NASA's Manned Spacecraft Center in Houston, Texas.

Seismic equipment to furnish information on the moon's interior structure.

Magnetometers and gravimeters to measure local variations in the moon's magnetic and gravitational fields.

Sampling containers and gas-analysis equipment to study the lunar atmosphere.

Early Apollo moon landings, limited to about 250 pounds of scientific gear, will not go far beyond the first landing in surface activities. These Lunar Modules will be unable to support a stay of more than forty-eight hours on the moon, and much of this time must be used to check out the craft for the flight back. Also, the stay must be limited to avoid fatigue. At the end of their two-week voyage to the moon and back, the crew will face the most strenuous, exacting, and critical maneuver of all—the precision approach and re-entry into the earth's atmosphere at a blazing 36,000 feet a second, more than 24,000 m.p.h. Main emphasis will be on demonstrating the feasibility of the flight itself.

Follow-on flights with more-advanced spacecraft will permit much longer stays on the moon. Increased payloads will provide moon explorers with really sizable tools (like deep-drilling rigs) and with vehicles to make extended trips afield from the landing sites. Then will come the heyday of lunar exploration.

One of two moon-landing concepts that look particularly promising is called the Augmented Lunar Module (ALM). It applies the fact that the Saturn V launch vehicle seems capable of hurling toward the moon a somewhat higher payload than was originally specified. This would allow some increase in the propellant capacity of the LM and, in turn, an increase in the useful load landed by the LM. Thus the life support for the astronauts—oxygen, water, food—could be extended for several days. More scientific equipment could be carried along to make those extra days worth-while.

The other concept envisions twin landings on the moon by an "LM Shelter" and an "LM Taxi." It would work as follows:

Two Saturn V/Apollo space vehicles are launched from the Cape, maybe weeks apart. The first carries a normal Apollo Command and Service Module and the usual crew of three. Upon arriving in orbit around the moon, the crew detaches and dispatches a special unmanned LM—the LM Shelter—to a predetermined landing spot and returns to earth.

This one-way LM Shelter consists of an unmodified LM descent stage and an LM ascent stage from which the propulsion system has been removed. Hence, it can land a payload equal to the full weight of a fueled and manned LM ascent stage (plus whatever weight a round-trip LM would leave on the moon).

A few weeks later the second Apollo spacecraft appears in orbit around the moon. Two of its three astronauts transfer from the Command Module to the LM Taxi and descend to the lunar surface. The LM Taxi differs from a normal LM only in that it can survive the lunar environment for an extended time without losing its capability of climbing back to the orbit around the moon.

Guided by a radio beacon on the LM Shelter, the LM Taxi touches down within a fraction of a mile from it. Then the shelter becomes the astronauts' lunar base. They return to the Taxi to depart.

A major attraction of the Shelter-Taxi concept is that the Shelter

An LM Shelter, landed on the moon before astronauts' touchdown, could become a base for a two-week stay. The shelter is an unmanned and modified Lunar Module.

This "Lunar Jeep" could be brought to the moon on the outside of the LM Shelter.

offers a habitable abode for a stay of weeks. Removing the ascent stage's propulsion system leaves room for the astronauts to sleep in hammocks, for instance, rather than rest in the rather awkward squatting position required in a normal LM. They would be able to get out of their space suits during rest periods. The feasibility of such a stay was illustrated in 1966 by a simulated moon mission of comparable length. In a cabin about the size of three telephone booths, built for the trial at Minneapolis by Honeywell, Inc., two Marshall Space Flight Center engineers successfully lived and worked for eighteen days, making space-suited excursions from time to time. Results of the test were equally applicable to the LM Shelter or to a mobile and enclosed lunar laboratory (which the design represented).

Another advantage of the one-way LM Shelter, with its great extra payload, is that it can bring along a "Lunar Jeep." This vehicle would extend the astronauts' radius of action from one or two miles to easily ten times as far.

An obvious disadvantage is that the Shelter-Taxi concept requires two successful landings at the same spot, while the Augmented LM provides a complete, if severely limited, scientific capability wherever it touches down. Views of lunar-surface features from Lunar Orbiter are expected to yield information that will help in choosing between the two approaches.

In the long haul, lunar-surface exploration will call for more-advanced hardware not included in the present Apollo program. For instance, if a Saturn V is employed solely to carry cargo on a

Saturn V-launched unmanned cargo landers could soft-land 30,000 pounds on the moon—opening the way to large stationary and mobile lunar labs and, ultimately, permanent manned bases.

one-way trip to a predetermined spot on the moon, neither the manned Apollo Command and Service Module nor an LM is needed. Instead, the unmanned flight could follow the successful Surveyor soft-landing pattern, with a newly developed high-energy braking system used for the final letdown. Such a transportation system could soft-land payloads of up to 30,000 pounds on the moon.

This capability, entirely within the reach of a standard Apollo/ Saturn V launch rocket, could truly put a new dimension in our lunar-surface activities. Mobile laboratories, capable of trips of several hundred miles across the face of the moon, would become a possibility. And permanently inhabited camps on the moon, comparable to our research camps in Antarctica, could become a reality within a few years after the first lunar landing.

How We'll Travel on the Moon

There will be several types of vehicles for traveling on the moon, used for several different applications.

Even before the first astronauts set foot on the moon, a small, fully automatic roving vehicle may have explored the immediate vicinity of the landing site of its unmanned carrier spacecraft. Remotely controlled by an armchair driver back on earth, who sees the lunar landscape roll past on a television screen as though he were looking through a car's windshield, such an automatic vehicle could furnish valuable information on the makeup of the moon's surface.

The initial manned lunar-landing attempt will undoubtedly involve so many pioneering firsts that the exploratory tasks to be performed by the astronauts on the lunar surface will be severely limited, simply to assure maximum chances of success. But to exploit fully the scientific possibilities opened by the spectacular first touchdown, subsequent landings will require two elements of support:

First, lunar shelters will be needed where the astronauts can get out of their space suits and rest.

Second, we must provide adequate ground transportation. The visible part of the moon extends over an area twice the size of the United States—and the far side of the moon is just as large.

For short-distance travel a nonpressurized "moon jeep" may suffice (See Chapter 37 "What We'll Do on the Moon"). The astronauts would hop onto its open platform and depend for protection upon their pressurized space suits, while life support and communication would be provided by their backpacks.

Longer surface journeys will require a pressurized vehicle that offers air-conditioned comfort in a "shirtsleeve" environment, and room for the exploreres to stretch out during rest periods. An airlock will be needed, to get in and out. The vehicle must be equipped with a two-way radio. And there must be ample facilities for research tasks en route.

As there are no superhighways on the moon (yet), all vehicles must have cross-country capability. Just as on earth some terrain on the moon is reasonably smooth and flat, while other parts are rugged and mountainous. It would be unrealistic to demand a lunar vehicle that could negotiate any and all surface conditions. Rather, we must rely on moon-circling photo satellites to scout for suitable access routes to lofty crater rims and other interesting objectives for surface expeditions. An ability to negotiate a slope of 15 to 20 degrees appears adequate for even the most demanding missions.

Caterpillar treads provide more traction than wheels, but at a cost of greatly increased horsepower. This, whatever power source we use, means more weight. And weight is a precious commodity on the moon, where every ounce will have to be shipped from earth—until we can produce our own fuel there, as some day we undoubtedly will.

Careful analyses show that under the "unearthly" conditions of the moon—where a 170-pound man weighs only 29 pounds—the wheel seems to have a decided edge over the endless track. A particularly intriguing concept for lunar surface vehicles is a wheel with elastic spokes (see my sketch, p. 168), which combines the advantages of a smooth ride with an enlarged traction area. For extra traction in soft terrain, lugs may be attached to the flexible wheel rims (or extended by pushbutton action), just as you would put snow chains on your tires.

To avoid bogging down in soft ground, the wheels must be large in diameter. By Detroit standards this will give moon cars a rather weird appearance (see my second sketch, p. 169).

As the moon has no atmosphere, conventional combustion engines are out. Solar batteries, such as power the instruments and radios of most of our unmanned satellites and deep-space probes, may at first blush look like an obvious source of cheap power on the cloudless moon. But they need about twenty-five square yards of area to produce one puny horsepower, and so a rather large energy-collecting "sail" would be required. While this is fine for a stationary power plant, it is not too compatible with the bumpy ride of a cross-country vehicle moving over rugged terrain. Moreover, solar batteries are ineffective during the lunar night—which, particularly during periods of bright "earthshine," may be a very attractive time for surface travel.

Nuclear power sources for vehicular application entail nasty radiation problems and do not look too attractive at this time.

Among the best bets seems to be the hydrogen-oxygen fuel cell. (See Chapter 18 "Space Power from Fuel Cells"). Remember the old physics-lab experiment demonstrating "electrolysis"? An electric current is sent through a tray of water, and the current breaks

up ("dissociates") the water molecules, with the result that hydrogen gas bubbles up at one electrode and oxygen gas at the other. In a fuel cell the process is just the other way around: Hydrogen gas and oxygen gas are fed into the cell, and out comes an electric current. The efficiency of the process is about sixty percent, which is better than that of our finest turbogenerators. (This is why industry has high expectations for the extended use of fuel cells in commercial power generation—another example of an invaluable "fallout" product of our space program.)

Fuel-cell power for lunar surface vehicles looks very attractive even for early applications, where the hydrogen and oxygen propellants must still be flown in from earth. At a later stage of lunar surface exploration, once we have a nuclear-power reactor on the moon (such as NASA's Snap 8 or Snap 50), we can easily produce hydrogen and oxygen from a lunar research station's waste water—or even from the "crystal water" that geologists believe can be extracted from lunar minerals.

Each wheel of the lunar surface vehicle would be powered by one or more electric motors, driven by current from the fuel cell. But since there is no atmosphere on the moon, we cannot air-cool these motors. This presents a serious problem, particularly for travel during a hot lunar day, when surface temperatures climb beyond 200 degrees F. The best solution seems to be to use ceramic insulating materials that will permit the motors to operate at temperatures of 400 to 500 degrees, where heat radiation will provide for cooling.

Lubrication poses another problem. Liquid lubricants (such as oil or grease) rapidly evaporate from bearings exposed to the hard vacuum of outer space. Dry lubricants (such as graphite or molybdenum sulfide) are not nearly as effective in a vacuum as in the atmosphere—where an air film gets between journal and bearing. Sealed, pressurized bearings are a possibility, but they are complex and troublesome. It is probably fair to say that while we have enough know-how to build adequately lubricated bearings for lunar surface vehicles of limited lifetime, there is much room for improvement and advanced concepts in this field.

Temperature control for the living and equipment spaces aboard a lunar surface vehicle suitable for long-distance operations poses another difficulty. Such a vehicle should be capable of day and night travel. During the fourteen-day lunar night we have no problem—as in an automobile, we can always tap a little power for heating, and it is easy to provide effective heat insulation. Cooling, wherever necessary, is just as easy, because the excess heat can be radiated out against the "heat sink" of the cold lunar surface (—240 degrees F.) and the even colder star-studded universe above it. But during the lunar day the moon's surface is blazing hot, far hotter than the 72-degree F. comfort temperature we propose to maintain in the vehicle.

The best answer seems to be a well-insulated vehicle, painted white or silver—to minimize its heating by radiation from the lunar surface—and equipped with an air-conditioning system that permits radiating the excess energy away at a temperature level elevated to several hundred degrees. The hot "heat-rejection surfaces" must be located on the vehicle's top, or possibly (if the vehicle is to descend deep into brightly sunlit lunar canyons) on parabolic dishes, which can be aimed like a radar antenna at a stretch of cold sky overhead.

VI. BONANZAS ON THE WAY TO THE MOON

Project Apollo-Saturn Will Pay Off

As a nation we are firmly committed, everyone knows, to Project Apollo-Saturn—the plan to land an American on the moon before this decade ends.

Less well-known is the fact that a successful lunar landing in this decade is not so much an end in itself, as a most effective focus for developing a broad U. S. manned-space-flight capability that will pay off in four major ways:

> Direct benefits to all mankind.
> Gains for our national security.
> Fundamental knowledge about the universe and its origin.
> Engineering and managing know-how.

The hard and simple specification of an early manned landing on the moon has served to put our manned space program into high gear. And it has assured continuing public and Congressional support. For it would obviously be foolish to spend so much for manufacturing, testing, and launching facilities if we were not determined to invest further funds to man those facilities—and see the gigantic Apollo-Saturn program through to a successful conclusion. The moon landing, however, has never been this program's sole objective.

When Lindbergh soloed the Atlantic in 1927, he announced that Paris was his goal. But if his aim had been only to get to Paris, he might as well have taken a boat. The real purpose underlying his flight was to demonstrate, in terms everyone could understand, that the time had come to fly safely across the Atlantic Ocean. We all know what happened to aviation after that.

Today we believe the time has come for man to venture safely farther away from earth than our astronauts' voyages in low orbits

The topography of the Arab Plateau in a Gemini photo.

so far. We think it is time to set foot on other heavenly bodies. The moon has become our cosmic Paris.

The payoff—as in Lindbergh's pioneering flight—will far exceed attainment of the immediate objective. Let us look into the four sorts of benefits I have named.

First will come direct help for our earthly endeavors.

Unmanned satellites already give us a preview: Syncom and Early Bird satellites provide global television, radio, and telephone service. Tiros and Nimbus satellites and the new operational Tiros system are about to become vital elements of a world-wide weather-forecasting network. Transit satellites furnish a useful navigation aid for ships, and more sophisticated ones can be foreseen for air navigation and traffic control.

Manned satellites, including orbital space stations, will perform more and more of these tasks in the future—and new ones, too. Putting men in orbiting vehicles will prove a great advantage in weather-advisory systems, and for the initial adjustment and later repair and maintenance of orbiting communications relays.

Man will play an even bigger role in orbital earth-observation posts to come:

Worldwide crop reporting from orbit can fill what will soon become an urgent need. Present trends of the population explosion indicate that the earth will have six to seven billion mouths to feed by the year 2000—and twice as many just 35 years later. The resulting problems of famines, strife, and struggle for sheer survival are not for the distant future to worry about but for our own children and grandchildren. We must learn how to manage our planet's resources better—and must find out first how much food is available and where.

Sophisticated aerial photography, it has been demonstrated, can clearly identify various crops. You can tell a rye field from a barley or oat field, a farm growing soy beans from one raising rice or corn. Moreover, you can distinguish a healthy crop from one affected by drought, or beset by stem rust or fungus. This method employs a series of films of different spectral sensitivity, and a battery of "remote sensors," simultaneously viewing the same spot on the earth's surface in different wavelengths of visible or infrared light. There is no reason to doubt that the technique, pioneered in

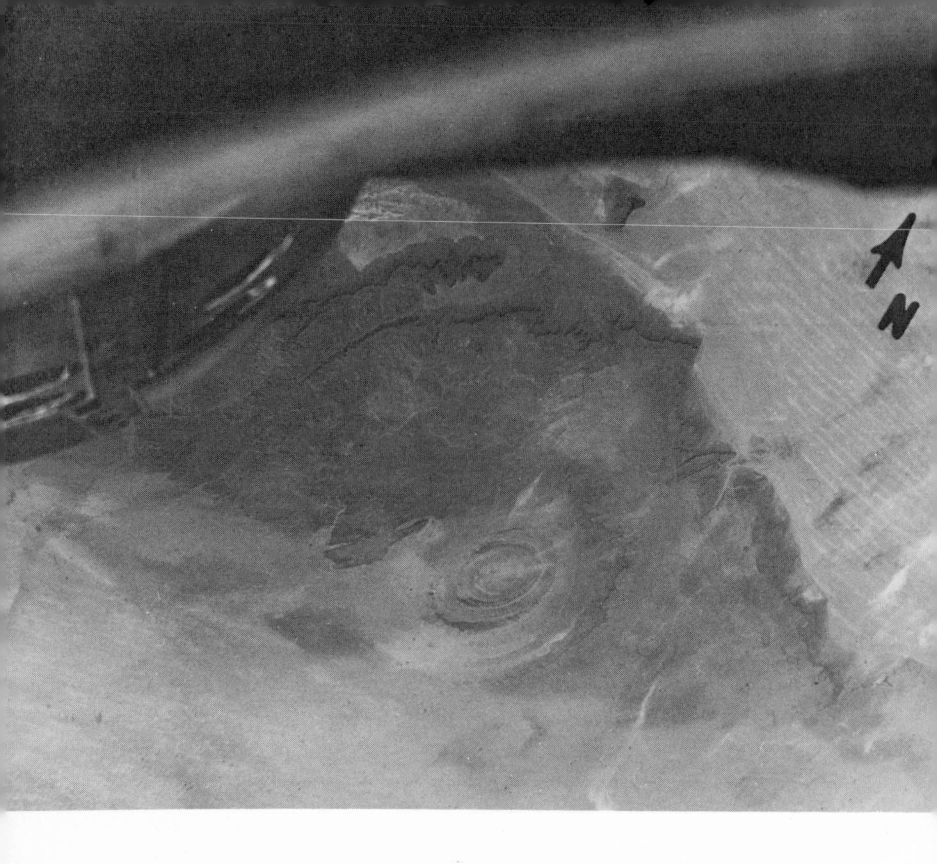

A mystery formation in Mauritania, possibly made by a meteor landing, is eyed from orbit. Such views of the earth's surface from space may aid geologists and prospectors.

airplane flights, could be used just as effectively from orbit.

Collecting crop data over the whole globe will need to be done continuously. Not only do plants change their appearance in growing; some weather-favored areas may be due for an exceptional yield, while other regions suffer from drought or floods. Only by keeping constant track of a given region will it be possible to come up with a realistic forecast for the current season's crop. To make such a continuous global survey with airplanes would run up an exorbitant fuel bill. To do it from orbit, year after year, really makes economic sense.

Once such a global survey exists, it can be used for other purposes as well. Systematic prospecting for oil and mineral deposits will become possible. In fact, it will become a necessity if we are to avoid our entire technological civilization coming to a screeching halt. For the world's industries are depleting the known deposits at an ever-increasing rate, as both the world population and its demands for better homes, cars, and appliances grow at an alarming rate.

A watch can be kept on volcanoes and other geologically unstable areas of the earth's surface, with an eye towards predicting eruptions or earthquakes. Systems can be provided to warn ships of icebergs, and thinly populated areas of forest fires. Observations of snowfall can give better forecasts for the water management of storage lakes, hydro plants, and irrigation systems.

Oceanography is another customer. Great possibilities await continuous global measurements of such phenomena as sea state, ice movements, water temperature, salinity (determined from orbit by polarimetry), and ocean-water coloration. (Green streaks indicate high plankton content and ability to support a greater fish population.)

Since we have no plans ever to place nuclear bombardment missiles in orbit, Saturn-Apollo is unlikely to add to our national deterrent power. But, just as we can observe crops, storms, snow, and ice movements at sea, it stands to reason that we can also keep a watchful eye on things of military importance.

Undoubtedly, one of the greatest sources of danger in the world today is the Communist regions' secretiveness and their aversion to any kind of mutual-inspection scheme, because it oftens compels Western statesmen to depend upon educated guesses or assumptions rather than factual knowledge. Better information of what goes on in their walled-off portions of the globe will benefit our and other countries' national security—and make this planet a safer place in the nuclear age.

Probably the most important truth man has learned, in the 10,000 years of his conscious history, is that it has paid him to satisfy his curiosity. The substance of what we call civilization—the house we live in, the clothes we wear, the ideas we pursue, the work we do, the car we drive, the books we read—can all be traced back to the simple fact that at some time someone was curious about something. Observing the universe from the vantage point of outer space—unobstructed by an atmosphere that blurs

The tip of the Arabian Peninsula is filmed by Gemini 4 with airplane-view clarity.

the stars' images and absorbs most of their radiation—is one of the best bets for man to enhance vastly his understanding of nature. It is up there that he may find the ultimate answer to what makes the universe tick.

Putting a man on the moon and bringing him back alive not only calls into play a host of scientific and engineering talents, it requires a refined approach to what is called systems analysis. This is the art of predicting what a change in performance or a defect, in one part or area, will do to other parts, other areas, and the whole system. Careful systems analysis permits us to find the best overall solution to a complex problem involving many different elements.

Entirely new management methods, too, have had to be developed. They enable the Apollo-Saturn managers to take prompt corrective action when something goes wrong in the complex machinery of an effort involving thousands of companies, hundreds of thousands of people, and hundreds of millions of dollars—and the entire, intimately interwoven program is in danger of falling out of step.

Many of these new managing techniques can be used to great advantage in fields as unrelated to space as high-speed interurban transit and causes and remedies for air and water pollution. They can even be adapted to human relations problems, such as racial unrest and juvenile delinquency.

So, in blazing a trail to the moon, we are opening bypaths whose exploration promises rich rewards to come.

We Need to Know More About the Sun

The sun is virtually the mainspring of life on earth. Not only does it furnish the necessary warmth to sustain life—without sunlight, there could be no photosynthesis, the basic process that enables plants to grow. And without plant life, there could be no animal or human life.

For many scientists the sun has another significance: It is the nearest of the billions of fixed stars—and therefore the one best suited for close scrutiny. By observing the sun, we may learn more of the physical phenomena at work throughout the universe.

To be sure, there are many kinds of fixed stars. The sun (a rather common type, class G) cannot furnish all the answers we seek. But it has already taught us much about the cradle-to-grave cycle that all stars seem to go through.

With our first Orbiting Solar Observatory successfully launched, and ever more elaborate ones on the way, we are hampered no longer by the "dirty basement window" of our atmosphere—and are bound to extend our knowledge of the sun vastly.

We have direct evidence that the visible surface of the sun could not possibly be solid: The sun rotates on its axis in roughly four weeks; but, while the equator takes about twenty-five days, the polar regions take thirty-one days. Actually the sun's surface temperature of 11,000 degrees F. makes it obvious that the sun must at least be enveloped in a layer of incandescent gas.

While this would not preclude the possibility that the invisible interior might be liquid or solid, there is other strong evidence to the contrary—the enormous amount of energy that the sun radiates continously. Its calculable rate is such that the sun's gaseous outer surface would have cooled off noticeably in just the last few hundred years, if its temperature had not been kept up by an even

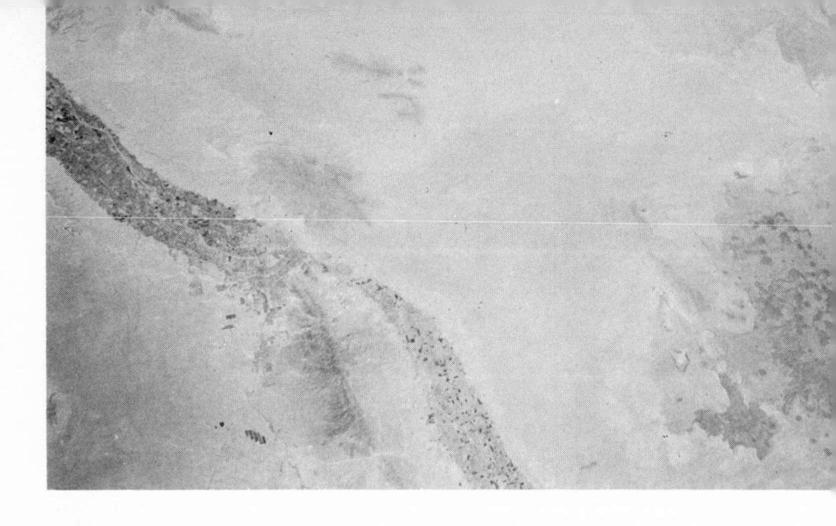

El Paso, Texas, streets seen in a view from more than 100 miles up in space.

hotter interior, so the sun's temperature must further increase as we descend from the surface toward the center.

This means, of course, that the sun must be a sphere of gas throughout—even if its central portion contains elements heavier than the hydrogen that predominates at the surface. Furthermore, there must be some mechanism to replenish those enormous energy losses.

It is now believed that the inner region of the sun (up to about twenty-three percent of the sun's radius) forms a huge thermonuclear reactor, where hydrogen is transformed into helium.

The temperature in the center of the nuclear-reaction zone is estimated at about 36,000,000 degrees F. Yet the pressure is so high, because of the sun's enormous gravitational field, that hydrogen gas (which makes up the bulk of the sun's mass) weighs about eighty times as much as water. Under these conditions the atoms are completely ionized or stripped of their electrons. They are also tightly spaced. Particularly the light protons, the ionized nuclei of the hydrogen atoms, whirl at tremendous speeds and collide often and vehemently enough to undergo "thermonuclear fusion" with heavier atoms. Such a fusion is accompanied by a release of energy which is radiated away and heats the surrounding gas. The end product of this process, during which hydrogen is consumed, is helium.

This "hydrogen burning" is quite a complex process. As Dr.

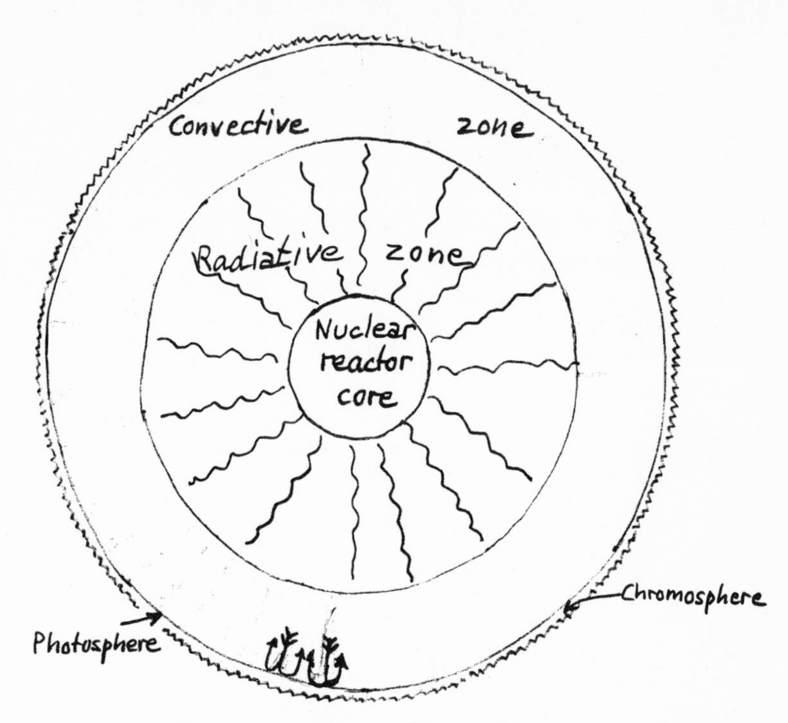

Cross section through sun.

Hans Bethe of Cornell University discovered, it involves atoms of carbon, nitrogen, and oxygen. But these atoms act only as intermediaries, or catalysts, and are completely regenerated at the end of the "circular Bethe reaction chain." The net result is that hydrogen is consumed, energy is released, and helium is produced. The Bethe process has been going on for several hundred million years. During all this time it has enabled the sun's surface to emit about 4.10^{23} kilowatts (that is a four with 23 zeros!) into surrounding space without cooling off. And yet, during the entire geological period, the sun lost only about one percent of its hydrogen content.

Within the sun's nuclear core and the area around it, the energy is radiated outward—in the form of X rays and gamma rays. Heat transfer by *radiation* is so dominant in this region, where temperatures exceed 1,000,000 degrees F., that convection can be disregarded.

At about seventy percent of the distance from center to surface, the temperature has dropped to about 250,000 degrees F., and the gas density to less than 1/10 of that of water. Under these conditions, radiation no longer can maintain the outward flow of energy, and *convection* now takes over the major role. Energy is carried by the buoyant upward motion of heated material, through a steep temperature gradient, somewhat like a cumulus cloud that is bursting into the colder upper atmosphere. Heated material that has already reached the surface, and has cooled off by radiating its energy away, descends back to the radiation zone through the spaces left between the billowing cumulus towers.

The top of this convection zone is the source of all visible sunlight. Magnified solar photographs clearly show the granular structure of the rising cumulus-like formations. Astrophysicists call this region the *photosphere*. It has a temperature of about 9,000 degrees F.

Immediately above lies the *chromosphere,* a turbulent layer of gases about 6,000 miles high, with a density of less than 1/1,000 as much as the photosphere. It is a seething mass of gaseous fountains heated to about 11,000 degrees F. It has been called the "spray" of the photosphere because it is kept in continuous motion by the heaving photosphere beneath.

Constant kicks by the fast-rising cumulus towers below send supersonic shock waves traveling across the chromosphere. These waves, dissipated in the chromosphere, account for its somewhat higher temperature. If we could lower a heat-resistant microphone into the chromosphere, it would undoubtedly tramsit a continuous roar of thunder. Despite the higher temperature, the chromosphere emits far less radiation than the photosphere, because of its lower gas density.

The corona is a huge layer of rarefied gas surrounding the sun and extending out to one or two solar diameters, with conspicuous streamers sometimes reaching far beyond. We see it during total eclipses, when the moon hides the sun from view. The corona's shape is greatly affected by the number of sunspots present.

The corona is only about 1/1,000 as dense as the chromosphere, but its temperature is of the order of 2,000,000 degrees F. Just as the photosphere heats the chromosphere by thrusting up its granules, so the chromosphere heats up the corona with supersonic gas bursts. The higher temperature in the corona is again accounted for by energy-dissipation of shock waves.

It is now generally accepted that a sunspot is formed whenever a strong local magnetic field arrests one or more of those rising cumulus granules in the sun's convective zone.

Once their convective movement is braked, local heat transport stops. The affected area cools down through radiation losses—and becomes a dark sunspot.

How do we know this? What is probably the most direct proof lies in the so-called Zeeman effect in the spectrum of the area around a sunspot. Seventy years ago the physicist Zeeman discovered that each of the spectral lines in the light emanating from a luminous gas (for instance, from a neon tube) split into two or three lines as soon as the gas was placed in a magnetic field. The spectral lines of light from the vicinity of a sunspot do just that. Magnetic-field strengths up to 3,000 gauss have been measured around some big sunspots. This is quite a bit when we consider that the earth's magnetic field, which turns our compass needles, has a strength of only a fraction of 1 gauss.

The hot "cumulus" gases, heaving up at supersonic speeds through the sun's convective zone, are still hot enough to be highly ionized or stripped of most of their electrons. Thus, they are very good electrical conductors. As the surrounding magnetic field induces a current in the rising gas column, the latter is braked to a halt, just like a copper disk rotating in a magnetic field.

About Comets and Meteors

A comet is a relatively small body moving in a closed orbit about the sun. The eccentric shape of its orbit and, of course, its tail, set a comet apart from a planet or an asteroid.

Comets so bright as to outshine all but the sun and moon may appear once or twice in a century. Others, fainter but visible to the naked eye, occur every few years. There are always a few comets in the sky that can be seen or photographed with powerful telescopes.

A comet has three visible parts. Its head, called the coma, forms a bright diffuse cloud. Within is a solid starlike nucleus, one to fifty miles in diameter. The tail, a comet's most conspicuous feature, looks like a stream of gas, always pointing away from the sun.

Near the aphelion—the point farthest from the sun in a comet's highly elliptical orbit—its nucleus is dim; there is hardly any coma, and never a tail. Only as the comet swings nearer the sun do things begin to happen. (see my diagram.)

First the solid nucleus surrounds itself with the nebulous coma. Then the tail develops. The comet becomes brightest and in fullest bloom near the perihelion, its closest approach to the sun. Unfortunately, it cannot then be observed too well from the earth's surface because the bright dawn or dusk sky interferes with the observation of an object so near the sun. Orbiting telescopes offer a promising answer.

Photographic and spectrographic studies have led Prof. Fred L. Whipple, head of Smithsonian Observatory, to propose a comet "model" that has found almost universal acceptance and that explains nearly all observed cometary phenomena.

The nucleus from which coma and tail arise, he suggests, consists of porous rock froth, impregnated with frozen water, ammonia, methane, and carbon dioxide. Far from the sun, this conglomeration is cold and dormant. But as the comet nears the sun, solar heat begins to vaporize the frozen gases. Some of this vapor forms the nebulous coma; the rest forms the tail, which is blown away from the comet by some repulsive force centered at the sun. One such force might be light pressure, exerted on matter by impacting photons. But this tiny force cannot explain all we observe:

First, the tremendously long straight streamers of some comets' tails could be caused only by a repulsive force many times stronger than light pressure. Second, some tails are curved, or have straight and curved portions. Third, all comets' tails are two-dimensional, being confined to the plane of the comet's orbit. This becomes dramatically apparent when the earth happens to pass through that plane: The tail abruptly disappears. It is as if a flat picture of it were turned edgewise to your eye.

To these puzzles spectral analysis provides a clue: The extremely tenuous gases of a comet's tail are almost completely ionized or electrically charged. This makes them susceptible to attraction or repulsion by electrostatic and magnetic fields.

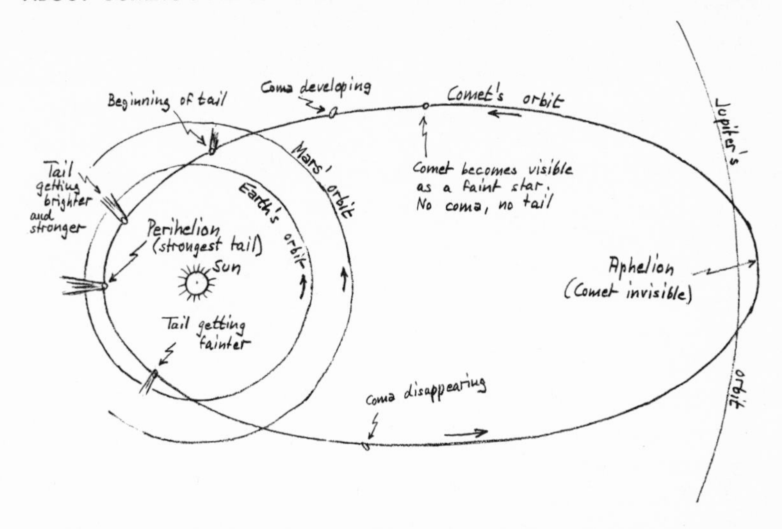

Now, the sun emits great streams of electrons and protons during rather frequent solar eruptions. As these electrostatically charged particles traverse space, they carry with them vast magnetic fields—and comets are bound to run into them. Thus, the varied forms of comets' tails result not only from solar light pressure but also from electrostatic and magnetic forces acting upon the ionized gases that comets' tails are made of.

Since a comet gives off matter, its life expectancy depends primarily on how fast it loses mass by evaporation—which, in turn, depends on how close it comes to the sun during perihelion passes. So its life is determined by its orbit.

Astronomers divide comets into a short-period group, taking less than two hundred years to complete their orbits; and a long-period group, taking more. Short-period comets seem to prefer orbits in or near the ecliptic, the plane in which the earth circles the sun. Long-period comets' orbital planes vary at random—and the lifetime of these comets is unknown, for the science of systematic comet observation is not yet even two hundred years old.

Jupiter, largest planet in our solar system, has a great effect on comets' orbits. Whenever a comet happens to pass near Jupiter, the planet's powerful gravitational pull will throw it off its path. Sometimes this increases the aphelion, the maximum orbital distance from the sun—and occasionally may even result in an escape trajectory taking the comet right out of the solar system. The most likely effect, though, seems to be a decrease of the comet's aphelion distance, for about half of all short-period comets have an aphelion close to Jupiter's orbit. The orbital period of comets like these is less than ten years.

Just as Jupiter's pull tampers with a comet's aphelion distance, it can reduce the perihelion distance—to the point where the comet may plummet smack into the sun and be consumed forever.

If the comet just grazes the sun, solar heating may still be so great that all frozen gases evaporate completely and are blown away in a gigantic tail. Even a good part of a comet's solid nucleus may also be vaporized.

A fly-by at somewhat greater distance may still result in solar tidal forces that rip a comet apart. Fragments of its solid nucleus will then enter the outbound part of the original orbit at slightly different speeds, which leads to slight differences in their orbital periods. Thus, after a number of revolutions, the material of the original nucleus becomes scattered all over the orbit. When the earth crosses the orbit of such a dissolved comet, we witness a meteor shower.

A meteoroid is an individual chunk of matter traveling through outer space. It may have a size anywhere from a dust speck to a block weighing several tons.

A meteor is a meteoroid that enters the earth's atmosphere. Heated by air friction, it causes the streak of light we see as a shooting star. Very bright meteors are often called fireballs.

A meteorite is an unconsumed portion of a meteoroid that reaches the ground.

Don't be too surprised, though, if you sometimes find these terms used with their meanings interchanged.

The speed at which a meteoroid may enter the atmosphere and become a meteor ranges from about seven to forty-five miles a second. The lower limit is set by the speed of a body falling from infinite distance under the pull of the earth's gravity, the upper limit by the combined speed produced by the sun's gravity and the earth's velocity in its orbit.

Meteorites found on earth must be distinguished as of "stone," "iron," and "intermediate" types. The relative abundance of these three kinds on earth does not necessarily prove, however, that the same ratio applies to pre-atmospheric meteoroids. Actually, there is evidence that a great many meteoroids break up in the atmosphere at relatively low dynamic pressures, showing their extreme fragility. Sizable pieces of such fragile meteoroids are much less likely to reach the ground than rugged chunks of stone or iron.

This has particular interest in connection with meteor showers —which, we have seen, occur whenever the earth crosses the orbit of a comet that has slowly disintegrated under solar heat and tidal effects. According to Whipple's "model," all that remains of its solid nucleus is highly porous material—and this could be expected to be fragile. So we may conclude that few if any of the meteorites we find on the ground are of cometary origin.

Ships and Planes Navigated by Satellites

Since July of 1964, the U. S. Navy has conducted extensive tests of a navigation system for ships that uses three satellites especially designed for the purpose. These Transit satellites were placed in near-circular orbits six hundred miles high by the time-tested Thor-Able Star rocket from Vandenberg Air Force Base on the west coast. The tests seem to have been highly successful, for the Navy recently declared the whole system ready for operational use.

How can satellites be used to navigate ships? The basic idea is simple:

A small satellite equipped with receiver, transmitter, and a signal-storage device is launched into orbit. Its orbital data, determined by ground tracking stations, are transmitted back to the satellite in suitably coded form—and stored, much as with a tape recorder, by a magnetic memory. Should the satellite gradually change its orbital path, the older information may be replaced by updated tracking data. Thus the satellite, whenever interrogated from the ground about its orbital path, is ready to give up-to-date information. This is the first half of the story.

The other half concerns determining the *relative* position between the satellite and a ship that seeks to learn its own *absolute* position on the globe.

This relative position is found by measuring the pattern of the so-called Doppler shift of the satellite's transmitter frequency. Radio Doppler shift is the electronic counterpart of the familiar acoustic phenomenon that the pitch of a locomotive whistle drops as the train passes you. While the train is approaching, the sound waves hit your ear at a frequency higher than that emanating from the whistle. As the train recedes, you hear a frequency lower than that of the whistle's original tone.

In the case of Transit, the pattern of the Doppler shift from high to low clearly shows the nature of the satellite's pass with respect to the ship. If the change from high to low is rather abrupt, the satellite is at a high elevation. If the change is more gradual, the satellite is lower above the horizon. In addition, the Doppler shift is greater in a head-on overhead pass than in a slanting pass.

A land surveyor finds his absolute position by measuring his relative position against several landmarks whose absolute position he knows. The navigational satellite is only one landmark whose absolute position we know. But, since it is moving with astronomical precision through a predictable, accurately surveyed orbit, it actually offers many precisely surveyed landmarks at different times during one overflight.

With the Doppler-shift data simultaneously providing the relative positions between ship and satellite, the absolute position of the ship can be determined exactly. The Navy says that a navigational fix taken with the Transit satellite system is accurate within about one-tenth of a mile. (Celestial navigation is consistently accurate only to within one-half mile.)

Shipboard equipment used in the Navy's operational Transit tests works automatically. It activates itself when the satellite approaches, receives both the Doppler shift and the satellite's latest orbital data, computes the "fix," and even types the results in latitude and longitude for the navigator.

On a production basis, the Navy estimates, the shipboard equipment could be built for about $12,000 a set. Thus, use of Transit satellites for navigation would be entirely within reach for commercial shipping. Since the system, as a Navy spokesman puts it, offers an "accurate, dependable, worldwide, all-weather, 24-hour-a-day passive navigational-fix capability," Transit should find a lot of takers.

One of the hottest customers, of course, is the Polaris submarine fleet. For the effectiveness of these missile-launching subs depends on accurate all-weather position information, gained without betraying the ship's location by sending radio signals.

The Transit system seems equally suited for use by aircraft. Potential advantages are obvious for military or commercial planes flying over oceans or large land masses without adequate (or cooperating) ground-based radio-navigation aids.

The navigation satellites weigh about 150 pounds, and thus require only modest boost power. For global capability they must be placed in polar or near-polar orbits, so that the spinning earth will expose its entire surface to the satellite. A series of suitably spaced satellites provides around-the-clock coverage.

Transit satellites have special features worthy of mention: They are "gravity-gradient stabilized," which means they apply the phenomenon that a dumbbell-shaped object placed in earth orbit tends to align itself in the direction of the earth's gravitational pull. Transit's transmitters are equipped with oscillators that stabilize the transmitted frequencies with an accuracy of one part in ten billion, for utmost precision in determining the Doppler shift.

The electronic equipment of two of the three Transit satellites is powered by an array of 18,000 solar cells. The third one uses a SNAP-9A nuclear-power source—an atomic battery in which heat from plutonium 238 is converted by thermocouples into about 20 watts of electricity. Both solar and nuclear power sources provide lifetimes far in excess of the Transit satellites' guaranteed two-year usefulness.

VII. TO THE PLANETS— AND BEYOND

The Riddles of Mars

When the planet Mars was in a particularly favorable position for observation in 1877, the Italian astronomer, Giovanni Schiaparelli announced the discovery of a network of very narrow and perfectly straight lines which seemed to crisscross the surface of Mars like a spider web. For want of a better word he called these lines "canali."

Schiaparelli's report, submitted without fanfare, caused a sensation and made the Red Planet the object of wide popular interest and speculation.

As other astronomers got into the act to verify (or refute) Schiaparelli's canals, a whole set of criteria for these mysterious lines emerged in the professional literature:

> Most canals, observers reported, followed great circles of the planet's sphere.
>
> First observed only in the bright ("desert") regions of Mars, the canals were found to cross some dark areas, too.
>
> In areas covered overnight by "snow" (now believed to be hoar-

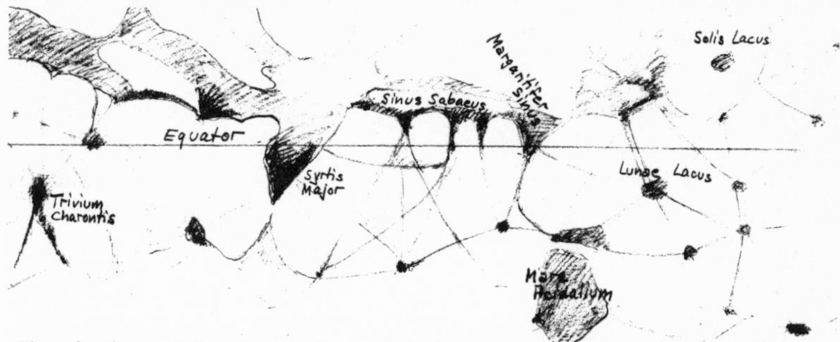

Sketch shows Mars's canals and dark areas as compiled from the observations of Schiaparelli and others. The main features are given their Latin names.

> frost), a canal was still clearly discernible, although its width was greatly reduced.
>
> All canals began and ended in dark regions, or in dark spots called "oases"; none was ever seen to disappear in a bright "desert" region.
>
> The canals' visibility was clearly linked to the seasons on Mars. As the white northern polar cap receded during the Martian spring, canals of the northern hemisphere increased in strength and contrast. Half a Martian year later, the same phenomenon took place in the southern hemisphere.
>
> During periods of seasonal strength, a strong canal would suddenly appear doubled. Where there had been a single great-circle line the night before, there would now be two parallel lines.

All these exciting observations inevitably led to speculation that the Martian canals might be the handiwork of highly intelligent beings. The flagbearer of this proposal was the American astronomer, Percival Lowell, one of the most outstanding planetary observers of all times. Mars was a dry planet, his reasoning went—well over half its surface was arid desert. Its main supply of water was available when its supposedly snow-covered polar caps melted during northern or southern springtime.

What would be more logical therefore, Lowell reasoned, than for Martians to develop a system of irrigation canals—to carry water from the melting polar snow caps to warmer latitudes, where food crops could be grown only if the ground were watered? To Lowell and his school, what they saw of a canal was not the water-carrying ditch itself—it would have had to be hundreds of miles wide to be seen with telescopes available then—but the bands of vegetation on both sides, like the green banks along the Nile or Rio Grande. Lowell's intriguing idea found worldwide support.

But, with the advent of more-advanced telescopes, it was finally shot to pieces. Using these more-powerful instruments, observers could clearly see much fine detail that had eluded the smaller telescopes of Schiaparelli and Lowell. Now a canal, instead of being a straight thin line, took on the appearance of a succession of irregular details.

Moreover, our present knowledge of Martian atmospheric pressure and surface temperatures precludes the possibility of open water.

We now know with a high degree of certainty that the small amount of water available on Mars is carried through the atmosphere in the form of ice crystals. Winds deposit this ice as hoarfrost in the polar regions during the winter months of the respective hemispheres. At winter's end the hoarfrost layer forming a polar cap has an estimated thickness of only a fraction of an inch.

However, the most up-to-date observations fully confirm the existence of predominant directions along which "activities" on the face of Mars are oriented. A canal is now looked upon as an axis along which is clustered a great deal of detail. Seasonal variations of the contrast with which this detail may be observed have likewise been fully verified.

Further, after many decades of carefully recorded observations of Mars, it has become quite evident that some previously reported areas of conspicuous detail and contrast have now become quite faint. Conversely, some formerly faint areas have become much stronger. And some areas, such as the Nepenthes-Thoth region, alternate between phases of great intensity and faintness.

Summing up, we can only say that the canals of Mars remain a riddle. Unlike the moon, which is a dead world, the surface of Mars shows seasonal as well as long-term changes.

Astronomers are extremely reluctant to answer the question of whether or not we will find life on Mars with a flat "yes" or "no."

The available evidence really is still too tenuous. In the past researchers were often carried away by their enthusiasm and strong convictions. Now, in this age of planetary rocket probes, they are painfully aware that they can no longer make pronouncements—which may be refuted tomorrow by overwhelming new evidence—with impunity.

The question of life on Mars centers about the planet's dark areas, whose contours change with the seasons. To explain why they do, three hypotheses have been advanced. Two are "non-vegetative," while the third ascribes the changes to some unknown type of vegetation.

First let us look at the so-called *volcanic* hypothesis. It proposes that suitably located volcanoes produce vast quantities of ash and cinders, more or less continuously. These are carried away by the winds prevailing at the season, and are deposited in certain stable and repeatable patterns. The trouble with this theory is that it calls for volcanoes different from any we know on earth, where none erupt steadily. Also, spectrographic studies of the Martian atmosphere fail to indicate the existence of large quantities of permanently suspended dust.

The *mineral-coloration* hypothesis, the second non-vegetative one, assumes a seasonal variation in the color of certain minerals that make up the dark areas. It is known that many "hygroscopic" or water-absorbing substances change in color according to how much water they soak up. As the prevailing winds carry Mars' scarce water supply in seasonal cycles between the northern and southern hemispheres, the theory goes, the changing humidity of the atmosphere alters the coloration of the material covering the surface of the dark areas.

This hypothesis has several moot points. On Mars, water does not rain out and "soak" the surface but is deposited in the form of ice crystals, as hoarfrost. And no known salts or minerals are noticeably changed in color by the minute quantities of water involved, even making the unlikely assumption that all the hoarfrost melted and was soaked up by underlying material. Finally, this hypothesis cannot explain the striking phenomenon of the dark areas' "regeneration":

Dust storms often are observed to deposit, on portions of dark areas, layers of the yellowish material that prevails in adjacent bright areas. But within a few weeks the dark area invariably regains its former contours!

Without some regenerative power (such as vegetative processes), it seems that any dark area would be buried miles deep under the yellow dust after millions of years of dust storms.

Finally there is the *vegetative* hypothesis—the one that assumes the existence of life on Mars. The dark areas, it suggests, are covered by some form of vegetation that withers during the fall. It snaps back in the spring when the temperature rises and the seasonal winds carry the humidity from the evaporating polar cap to lower latitudes.

The weakest point of the vegetative hypothesis is Mars' inhospitable climate. The French astronomer, Gerard de Vaucouleurs, probably the greatest living expert on Mars, once described it this way: "Take a desert on earth, shift it to the polar regions, and lift it to stratosphere level—that's what it is like on Mars." And there seems to be little or no oxygen (no more than 0.15 percent, by the best estimates) in the Martian atmosphere, which consists almost wholly of nitrogen.

Can life, as we know it, exist under such conditions?

Many biologists believe that certain low forms of earthly life such as lichens, microscopic algae, and bacteria would indeed survive if transplanted to Mars.

But must life on Mars be limited to these lowest forms? Look at the tremendous variety of forms of life on earth—in the water, on dry land, in the air. It may well be that during millions of years of evolution life on Mars has developed its own drastically different forms. Therefore the term, *life as we know it,* may indeed be too restrictive for the answer we seek.

Also, we must keep in mind that all available data on conditions on Mars are averaged over large areas. It is entirely possible that in limited areas conditions exist which are quite different from the average.

For instance, Mars may well have a rather hot interior, heated by radioactive decay of certain materials in its core. There is also a distinct possibility of the existence of permafrost, *i.e.,* permanently frozen water covered with layers of soil or sand. If these two assumptions are correct, it would appear entirely possible for local volcanic activities to melt enough permafrost and raise soil temperatures sufficiently to create "oases" of higher forms of vegetation.

In 1956, and again in 1958, the American astronomer, William M. Sinton, discovered certain "absorption bands" characteristic of organic molecules in the infrared spectrum of the dark regions of Mars. These bands also are observed in the spectrum of light reflected by vegetation on earth. Many astronomers think this discovery provides almost final proof of the existence of plant life on Mars.

Nevertheless, for a definitive answer, it is still safer not to embrace this conclusion—but to await the telemetered messages and televised pictures radioed back by our forthcoming Mars probes.

On July 14, 1965, the first successful Mars probe, Mariner IV, passed the planet at a distance of 6,118 miles and radioed a total of twenty-one still pictures of varying quality back to earth. Among much surface detail, the pictures revealed the existence on Mars of large craters which do not look too different from those on the moon. Some Martian craters and mountain rims seemed to be covered with ice or hoarfrost. By and large, the very limited swath of land photographed was more mountainous than expected. While the photos failed to give conclusive evidence of the existence of the controversial "canals," some astronomers believe they have identified at least one "canal" on one of the pictures. According to their interpretation, this particular canal is a strip of depressed land, or a canyon, several miles wide and half a mile deep enclosed by two parallel escarpments, which rise to the elevation of the surrounding high plateau.

While Mariner IV thus provides us with a few new answers about Mars, it has raised even more new questions. Mars is as challenging as ever. More sophisticated Mariner probes, unmanned Voyager spacecraft, which will repeatedly orbit Mars and soft land on Mars' surface, will furnish much new information. If what these vehicles find is interesting enough to warrant a personal look-see, man himself will undoubtedly set sail for Mars.

When Will We Land on Mars?

To arrive at an estimate of the time and effort required to prepare a manned expedition to Mars, we must first examine such things as the distance, travel time, and flight plan in more detail.

Place of departure. It is fairly certain that a manned Mars expedition will not start from the earth's surface, but from a low "departure orbit" around the earth. There, the interplanetary ship will be assembled, from modular loads hauled up by earth-to-orbit cargo rockets.

Size of crew. A Mars expedition may require a crew of six to ten, or more. For an interplanetary voyage, there are several arguments for a bigger crew than the trio of astronauts who will make the much-briefer Apollo moon trip. The length of the Mars expedition increases the chances that a crew member might become sick and require a doctor's care, as well as replacement. Adding a few crew members can give the expedition much greater scientific usefulness. And since the equipment will be more complex than for a moon trip, it will need more monitoring and maintenance.

The interplanetary rocket ship. For its power maneuvers, in earth orbit and near Mars, we can assume that the spaceship will be designed to use one of these two forms of propulsion:

High-energy chemical engines burning liquid hydrogen and liquid oxygen.

Nuclear engines, of the Rover type with a solid core, using liquid hydrogen as the sole propellant. These would provide nearly twice the "specific impulse" (a measure of propulsive efficiency) of high-energy chemical engines.

Payload. Besides the weight of the ship itself, its crew, and its

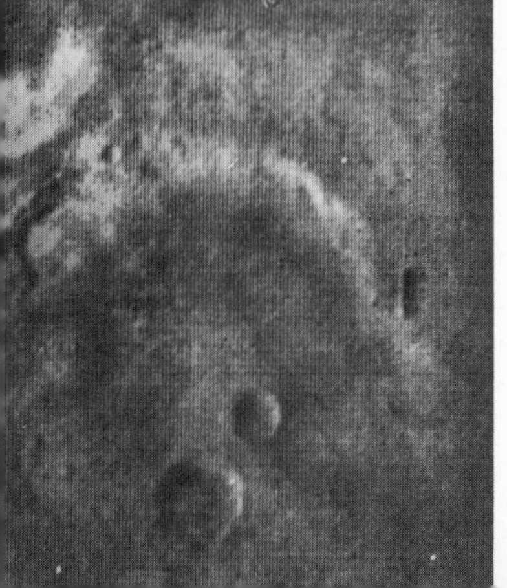

Mariner IV photo showing a crater landscape on Mars, with snow or hoarfrost covering the uplands.

propellants, we shall have to plan for sizable items of payload, including:

Enough oxygen, food, and water to supply all the crew members for the duration of the expedition.

A simple radiation shelter—since bursts of solar radiation, reasonably predictable for short periods like that of an Apollo round trip to the moon, cannot be forecast for the long time span of a voyage to a planet and back.

A spinning crew compartment to provide artificial gravity, or at least a centrifuge for occasional exposure to it.

Radio equipment capable of covering interplanetary distances reliably and with high data rates.

To arrive at any estimate of what all these items will total, we must now examine such things as the distance, time, and flight plan in more detail.

Distance. Comparison with a flight to the moon will help to put an interplanetary flight in perspective. The average distance between earth and moon is 238,860 miles, and a typical Apollo trajectory is only slightly longer.

Mars' closest approaches to earth are 35 million miles. But Mariner IV had to travel along a curved circumsolar trajectory of 325 million miles before getting there.

Flight times. A typical one-way flight to the moon requires two-and-a-half to three days. Mariner IV was on its way to Mars for eight months. These are one-way flight times. However, nobody wants to go on a one-way trip into space.

A typical Apollo round trip to the moon, including a twenty-four-hour surface stay, will last about ten days A typical estimate of round-trip flight time for a manned expedition to Mars is four hundred to four hundred fifty days, including a twenty-day stay on Mars. This takes into account the fact that, to get back from another planet with a reasonable expenditure of propellants, the return flight must be made when that planet and the earth are in reasonably favorable positions in their orbits.

Velocity requirements. To reach the moon, a spacecraft must acquire a speed just a trifle less than the earth's escape velocity, which is the speed required to escape permanently from the earth's gravitational pull.

For a one-way flight to Mars, the spacecraft need not reach a

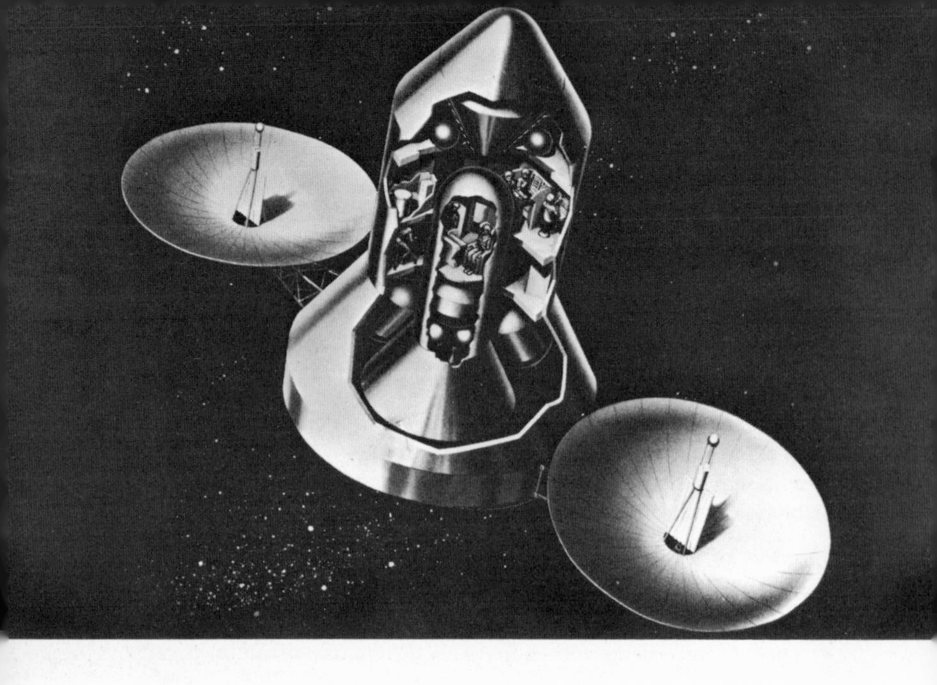

A NASA drawing of the "Mars Mission Module." It is a manned earth-to-Mars spacecraft containing two other capusles: an excursion module for the descent to the surface of Mars and a re-entry module for a return to earth. The dish-shaped appendages extended at the sides of the module are solar collectors for generating power on the long interplanetary voyage.

very much higher speed. Just a trifle *more* than escape velocity suffices to carry it out of the earth's field. The spacecraft will enter a circumsolar orbit that will carry it farther away from the sun (for instance, to Mars) if the excess speed is in the direction of the earth's orbital motion around the sun. The actual velocity at which the spacecraft enters its trajectory to Mars will equal the earth's own tremendous orbital speed, 18½ miles a second, plus that small excess speed with respect to the earth.

For the return trip, the velocity requirements are of the same order of magnitude as for the outbound voyage. But every ounce of rocket propellant to be consumed in leaving Mars represents payload for the outbound leg of a Mars expedition's journey—and many more ounces of propellant must be consumed to get it there. This is a fundamental difference between the power requirements for a one-way and a stopover round-trip interplanetary mission.

Landing on a planet. For man to set foot on a planet, he must

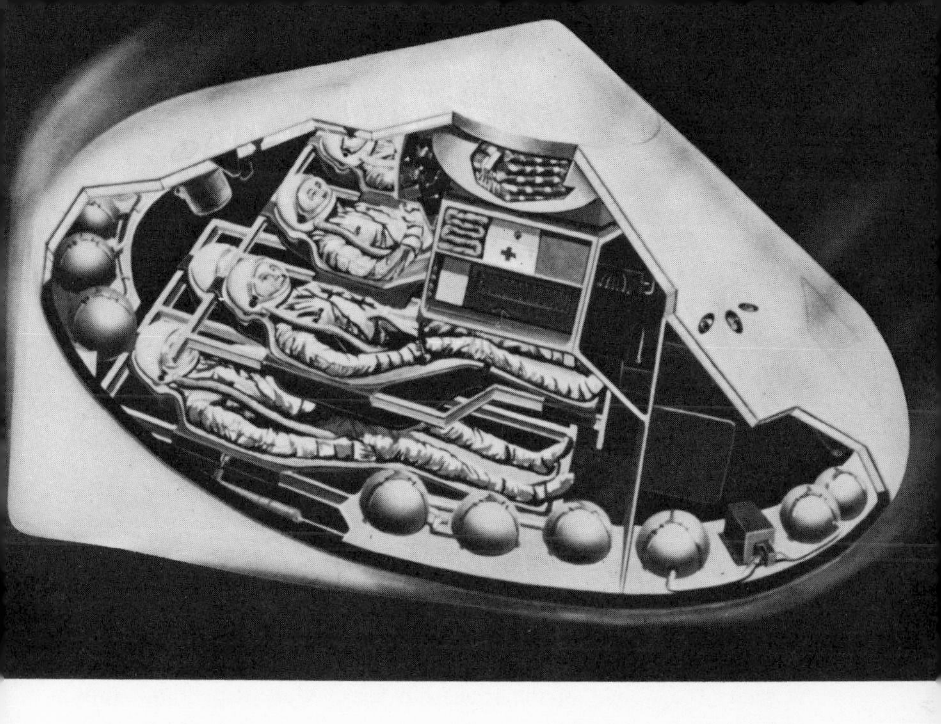

For the full-speed re-entry crewmen lie on couches arranged in two tiers to take G forces on hitting the earth's atmosphere in this NASA drawing of a Mars's expedition re-entry capsule. By dispensing with rocket braking, no propellants for the braking have to be hauled all the way to Mars and back.

first retard his spacecraft so the planet can "capture" it. From the resulting orbit around the planet, the explorers can then descend to its surface in a landing capsule that, of course, must provide rocket propulsion for re-ascent to orbit when the surface mission is completed.

In principle this resembles the lunar landing and re-ascent with the Apollo "Bug." In landing on a planet with an atmosphere, however, judicious use of aerodynamic braking can conserve the expedition's supply of rocket propellants.

Re-entry. Using aerodynamic braking to save rocket propellants becomes particularly important during the terminal maneuver of a Mars expedition—the return into the earth's atmosphere.

Reaching another planet takes more than earth-escape velocity, we have noted; and a returning spacecraft will likewise approach the earth's atmosphere with a speed in excess of earth-escape velocity. Thus return from Mars or Venus will always be at higher velocity than the sub-escape speed at which an Apollo Command Module returns from the moon. The constraints imposed on manned interplanetary expeditions by the relative motions of earth and the target planet, in combination with the desire to minimize the total round-trip travel time, compound to make the return velocity from Mars substantially higher than the return velocity from the moon.

If we can build a Command Module for a Mars expedition that can safely withstand the higher re-entry speed, we can avoid having to slow it down with rocket power to sub-escape speed as it approaches re-entry. This would be of great practical significance —for any power braking would have to be done with propellants hauled all the way to Mars and back, just for this final maneuver. Fortunately it looks as if such super-escape-speed re-entry capsules can indeed be built.

How it adds up. From all the foregoing facts, we can now estimate the weight of the spaceship for a Mars expedition, fully loaded and ready to go.

For a specific example, let us take a Mars expedition with a crew of eight men, a favorable opportunity such as 1986, a stay on Mars of about twenty days, and "full-speed" aerodynamic re-entry into the earth's atmosphere. We then find:

The departure weight of the fully loaded and fueled all-chemical interplanetary ship will be about 4,000,000 pounds. The figure for the all-nuclear ship will be about 1,600,000 pounds. That is what must be carried up by cargo rockets and assembled in earth orbit.

Let us assume these cargo rockets are outgrowths of Saturn V's, the most powerful type under development today. Saturn V's earth-to-low-orbit payload capability is about 250,000 pounds—which in due time can probably be stretched to 330,000 pounds so that three of these advanced Saturn V's would lug a million pounds of cargo into orbit.

Thus, twelve of the advanced Saturn V's could haul the weight of the chemical Mars ship into earth orbit—and five of them, the nuclear Mars ship. However, the number of supply flights actually needed may be twice as high, due to the extended duration of the orbital assembly operation—which leads to propellant-evaporation losses and requires assembly-crew rotation.

The figures are high, though not prohibitive. In space, as elsewhere, we must learn to crawl before we can walk—and obviously we have a lot to learn before we can begin to think of mounting a manned interplanetary expedition.

How far along are we?

Launch vehicles and spacecraft for a manned landing on the moon are rapidly approaching reality. Rocket engines and guidance equipment are in an advanced state of ground and flight testing. First flyable Saturn V stages have reached the launch facility, and Apollo spacecraft modules have been flown successfully.

Soon an Advanced Saturn I rocket will loft the first manned Apollo spacecraft into earth orbit. Before the end of this decade, if all continues to go well, a huge Saturn V rocket will hurl three astronauts in a similar spacecraft into a trajectory to the moon.

And the launch date for the first manned Mars expedition? Maybe 1986 wouldn't be a bad year, from all angles.

Atomic Power for Rockets

In essence a nuclear rocket engine is a reactor, perforated by narrow channels into which liquid hydrogen is pumped. When control rods are withdrawn, a neutron chain reaction makes the reactor white-hot. The control rods' action holds this temperature level.

Fed by a turbine-driven pump, liquid hydrogen flows first

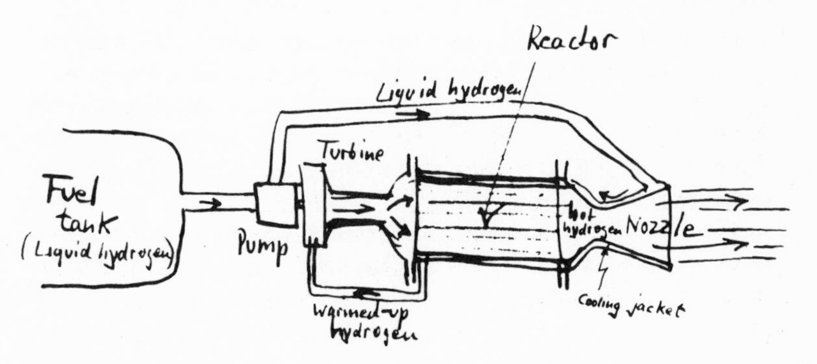

through passages for cooling the exhaust nozzle and the reactor's pressure vessel. Still pretty cold but already gasified, it enters the reactor. In the reactor's tubular channels, the hydrogen is heated to a temperature of several thousand degrees. Then it spurts from the exhaust nozzle.

Because of the very low molecular weight of hydrogen, exhaust velocity is very high, and this means a most economical use of propellant.

The heart of a nuclear-rocket engine, then, is the reactor that converts nuclear energy into heat and makes it go.

The fuel consists of a special kind or "isotope" of uranium metal, called U-235. When properly bombarded with neutrons, the uranium nuclei break up or "fission" into a pair of fragments apiece—and emit more neutrons in the process, thus keeping the reaction going.

The fission process releases energy, because the sum of the binding energies required to hold together the two fragments is less than the binding energy of the original U-235 nucleus. The excess energy is carried away by the pairs of fragments, by the neutrons, and by gamma rays. Since all of the fragments and most of the neutrons and gamma rays are stopped within the reactor, the bulk of the energy that is released by U-235 fission will heat the reactor.

For a nuclear-rocket engine to be thermally efficient, the reactor's temperature must be as high as possible. The melting point of uranium, 2,070 degrees F., sets a theoretical limit. Graphite, which withstands far higher temperatures, makes a very good material for the reactor's "moderator," which slows down ejected neutrons to a speed at which they are more likely to trigger more uranium fissions. So all present experimental reactors for nuclear-rocket engines are made of U-235 metal powder embedded in graphite.

For the reactor to operate at a constant power level, an average of exactly one neutron from each fission must cause another fission. All excess neutrons must be otherwise disposed of.

In a given nuclear-rocket engine design, a more-or-less fixed percentage of neutrons is lost through leakage to the outside and, particularly, through particle absorption not leading to fission. The remaining neutron balance can be adjusted with control rods of neutron-absorbing material, by varying the depth of their insertion in the reactor.

This control problem is greatly simplified by the fact that some of the neutrons (a little less than one percent) are "delayed"—emitted, not at the instant of fission, but over a period of seconds afterward. This permits us to use relatively sluggish controls to keep the reactor at the desired power level.

Just as in a chemical rocket engine, liquid-hydrogen propellant is pumped into the cooling jacket of the engine's exhaust nozzle. Gradually warming up, it flows upward through a "reflector" (which reflects outward-bound neutrons back into the reactor) to the engine dome, where it is turned around.

By now a cold gas, the hydrogen enters several hundred narrow passages drilled through the graphite-uranium reactor core—and is heated almost to the white-hot reactor's operating temperature. Emerging from the passages, the hot gas expands through a conventional DeLaval nozzle, in which it attains supersonic speed. The exhaust of a nuclear-rocket engine reaches 25,000 to 30,000 feet per second.

In terms of propellant economy, this means we get almost twice as much thrust out of every pound of propellant pumped in, as from a rocket engine using chemical combustion of hydrogen and oxygen.

A nuclear-rocket engine poses radiation problems, but it need not cause unacceptable hazards.

Probably the nastiest radiation problem is that the engine remains "hot" even after being shut down. The viciously radioactive atomic fragments created by the fission process keep emitting beta and gamma rays, which taper off only over a period of weeks and months.

This means that, unlike chemical engines, nuclear-rocket engines cannot be personally inspected after a static run. They must be placed in "hot cells" where they can be viewed only through multilayered shielding windows, and disassembled or worked on only with remote-control manipulators. Even tankage used during static runs must be detached from the engine and sent to a "cool-down" facility before it can be moved back into a normal assembly shop. This situation makes it virtually impossible to static-test a nuclear-rocket engine prior to its shipment to the launch site.

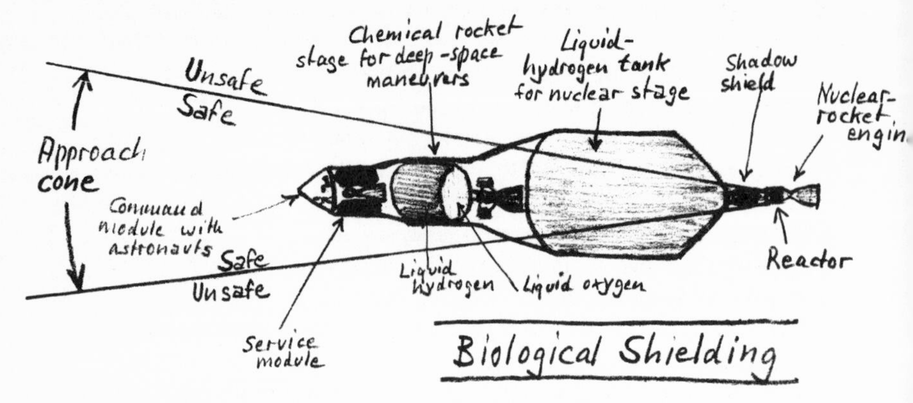

Another radiation problem involves the safety of astronauts riding a nuclear rocket. While inside their spacecraft in the rocket's nose, they are protected by a substantial amount of radiation-absorbing material, located between them and radiation from the engine. This material can greatly reduce the weight of the "shadow shield," which, as my sketch shows, must be placed directly above the engine.

However, many uses of nuclear rockets will involve rendezvous maneuvers in orbit, as for changing ships, changing crews, and orbital refueling. Approach for rendezvous and docking will be permissible only through the protected "approach cone" shown in my sketch.

Next, radiation causes a heating problem for parts near the rocket's engine.

A nuclear-rocket engine that produces one hundred tons of thrust runs at a reactor power level of several million kilowatts. In a well-built nuclear-rocket engine, only about one percent of the energy escapes in the form of gamma and neutron radiation, but, for the power level cited, that still amounts to tens of thousands of kilowatts! Think of the heat radiated even by a puny 100-watt lamp, and it is easy to understand why parts near a nuclear-rocket engine may need active cooling by suitable routing of the flow of liquid hydrogen to the engine.

Aside from its heating effects, the radiation emitted by the reactor has a rather unwholesome effect on many construction materials used in rockets. Metals behave reasonably well, but the lifetime of organic and plastic materials such as rubber, teflon, or polyurethane is greatly reduced, and even glass loses its transparency rather rapidly. Particularly vulnerable are electronic solid-state devices such as transistors, which must either be banned from nuclear rockets or put in heavily shielded boxes.

Interestingly, the dreaded "fall back," or explosion on the launch pad, constitutes no serious radiation hazard—simply because all nuclear rockets are likely to be chemically boosted off the launch pad anyhow. So the reactor, never having been operated, is free from dangerous radioactive fission products.

But special precautions are needed to keep a nuclear reactor from falling into the sea. Water entering the tubular channels in which hydrogen passes through the reactor core can drastically upset the delicate neutron balance—with the result that the reactor may "go critical" and destroy itself. While the energy released in such an incident would not be comparable with that of an atomic bomb, the effect would still be a low-yield explosion, accompanied by a formidable burst of neutron and gamma radiation. To prevent such an occurrence in case of a launch mishap, provisions for emergency destruct of the reactor may be a mandatory requirement.

A nuclear-rocket engine cannot be abruptly started and shut down. The tremendous difference between the original temperature of the liquid hydrogen (—423 degrees F.), and the white-hot temperature at which the reactor operates under full power, makes it necessary to start a nuclear-rocket engine relatively slowly. Otherwise, cracks in the reactor's brittle graphite-uranium core are unavoidable. Moreover, the increase in hydrogen flow through the reactor (controlled by the liquid-hydrogen feed pump) must be carefully synchronized with the increase in the reactor's power level (controlled by the position of its neutron-absorbing control rods).

Reactor shutdown poses an even more severe problem. During power operation, the reactor has contaminated itself with highly radioactive fission products. For a few minutes these keep emitting such a strong "decay radiation" that the reactor core would soon be heated to destruction unless one kept up an adequate flow of hydrogen through its passages.

This "aftercooling" of nuclear-rocket engines is not necessarily

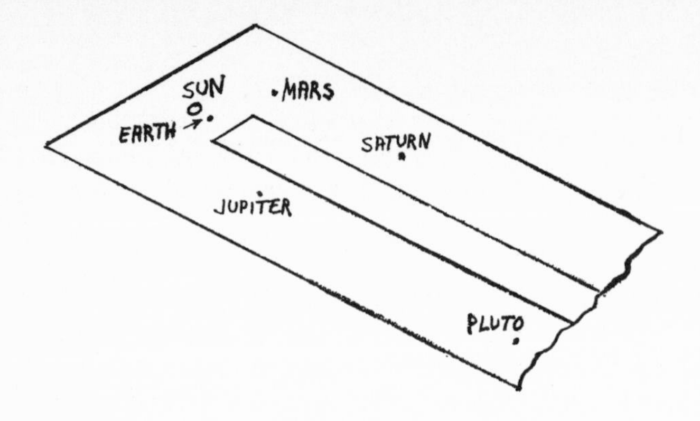

To imagine the distance to a star—this scale drawing with the sun and earth 1/8 inch apart would have to be extended more than a half-mile to show the distance to the nearest star.

wasteful. How much hydrogen will be needed to prevent the core from overheating is known beforehand. Thus, on a typical space mission, one would shut down the nuclear engine shortly before the required flight velocity had been reached. The missing balance of the speed would be produced by the exhaust of after-coolant heated by the decay radiation.

The most promising uses for nuclear rockets seem to be:

For upper stages of large chemically-boosted rockets, particularly in missions requiring very high final velocities.

For supply vehicles shuttling back and forth between a low earth orbit and an orbit around the moon (with hydrogen reloading during each stopover in earth orbit).

For planetary space vehicles beginning their voyages in earth orbit. These vehicles may be assembled in orbit from parts and propellants brought up by several chemically powered rockets.

Can We Ever Go to the Stars?

The past twenty years should have taught us to use the word "impossible" with utmost caution. Nevertheless, human travel beyond our own solar system is a staggering concept. Even the most reckless optimists do not expect it to come about in our generation —or the next.

Light, traveling at 186,000 miles per second, needs 8.3 minutes to span the 93 million miles between the sun and earth. Light takes

5½ hours to travel from the sun to Pluto, outermost planet of our solar system. But it takes 4.3 years to reach Alpha Centauri, the nearest fixed star (4.3 light-years away); 470 years to Polaris; and 27,000 years to get to the center of our galaxy—a lens-shaped island in space, a little less than 100,000 light-years in diameter, made up of an estimated total of some 200 billion suns.

To build a rocket powerful enough to travel so far is also a staggering concept. We have to impart to an object a velocity of slightly more than 25,000 feet per second to place it in a low orbit around the earth. About 36,000 feet per second is needed to hurl it to the moon—which is still within range of the earth's pull—and just a trifle more to kick it completely out of the earth's gravitational field. If we accelerate it up to a terminal speed of 56,000 feet per second (in such a fashion that it leaves the earth in the same direction in which the earth is orbiting at 107,000 feet per second around the sun), it will enter a parabolic flight path and escape from our solar system.

From the point of view of power requirements, a needed velocity of 56,000 feet per second (38,000 m.p.h.) may not sound too bad. Just one extra stage on top of the Saturn V, our Apollo moon rocket, could impart that speed to an object of about 8,000 pounds. And if we timed our launching in such a way that the receding uppermost stage gets a suitable "boost assist" by Jupiter's powerful gravitational field, we could even double that payload. But as the object coasted, its power spent, on its "uphill" path out of the pull of the sun's gravity, its speed would gradually diminish almost to zero. Millions of years would elapse before it reached one of the nearest fixed stars.

To reduce travel time to figures compatible with the life span of man, travel speeds must approach the speed of light.

Not even nuclear-fission or nuclear-fusion processes are ade-

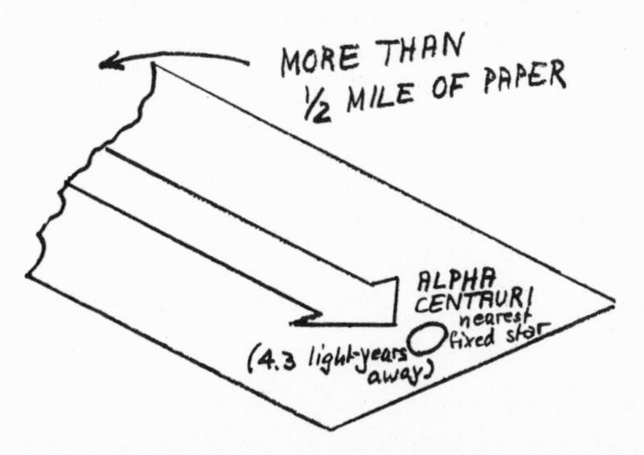

quate to produce such speeds. For all their dramatic display of power, they convert only a tiny fraction of the mass involved into energy. It would be necessary to devise a rocket mechanism wherein the *entire* mass, M, of the injected "propellant" is converted into radiation energy, E, according to Einstein's famous equation: $E=M \times C^2$. The exhaust of such a "photon rocket" would be a beam of radiation, and the exhaust velocity would of course be equal to the velocity of light, C.

The problem is that nobody knows how to build a photon rocket. Certain subatomic processes are known, such as the joining of an electron (a small negatively charged particle) with a positron (an equally small positively charged particle), that directly transform matter into energy according to Einstein's equation. But so far physicists have been unable to devise any large-scale processes for this transformation.

There are also tremendous engineering obstacles. By definition, a photon rocket converts its propellant stream into an extremely powerful light beam. To bundle this beam, some sort of mirror is needed. Even if it had a reflectivity of ninety-nine percent, better than our best existing ones, that one percent of absorbed radiation energy would instantly melt the mirror—considering the billions of kilowatts converted into the power carried away by the light beam.

It is impossible to exceed the speed of light. But, as we shall see, this statement is partly a matter of definition. Suppose we had overcome the "minor" problems just described and we did have a rocket capable of "beaming away" a hundred percent of the mass of its propellant with an exhaust velocity equal to the speed of light. What could we do with it?

If the rocket had a mass ratio (the ratio between its fully fueled and empty weight) of 3, it could reach 80 percent of the speed of light. With a mass ratio of 10, its terminal velocity would be about 98 percent; and with a mass ratio of 1,000 (about what we have today in some of our chemical multistage planetary rockets), we would hit 99.9998 percent of the speed of light.

Again we refer to Dr. Einstein. His Theory of Relativity (which has stood the test of many critical experiments and has been universally accepted by the scientific community) shows that *the inertia of an object's mass approaches infinity as the object ap-*

proaches the speed of light. Hence, it would take infinite power to accelerate an object beyond the "light barrier."

But, amazingly enough, the same theory states that a stellar astronaut could still travel to a star a thousand light-years away and return within his adult life.

Yes, incredible as it may sound, an astronaut could travel 2,000 light-years in a lifetime. "Time dilation" would help him to stay young. For many people, the strange phenomenon called time dilation is a hard pill to swallow. The flow of time appears to us completely unaffected by physical conditions. Whether we sleep or work, sit at a desk or in a speeding jetliner, our wrist watch seems to tick away at the same pace. So does our heart.

But the fact is that this cherished piece of "everyday experience" is valid only in the realm of relatively low velocities in which we slowpokes live.

A meson (an unstable subatomic particle), when traveling at a velocity close to the speed of light, has a clearly longer decay time than its 2.1-microsecond "half-life" at lower speeds—when an earth-fixed observer does the timing. But if the observer were flying along with the meson, the half-life of 2.1 microseconds would not seem to be affected by the particle's speed, since the observer's watch would be subjected to the same time dilation as the meson itself.

The Theory of Relativity tells us that the pace of time becomes slower and slower for an object approaching the speed of light, compared with time's rate of passage for a stationary observer. At the speed of light itself—an upper limit that no object can ever reach—time would come to a complete standstill. If an object could go so fast, it could cover vast distances while, for a man flying along with it, no time would elapse—neither for his watch nor for his heartbeat, which controls his life span.

This strange effect makes it possible for a stellar astronaut to travel from the earth to a fixed star a thousand light-years away in what he would think was 13.2 years. For the trip back he would need another 13.2 years. If he didn't spend any additional time at his destination he would thus have been away from the earth for 26.4 years. The trouble is that, during his absence, more than two thousand years would have elapsed on earth. Thus, upon return, he might wind up in a zoo.

Let us assume we have a photon rocket capable of a continuous acceleration of 1 g. Suppose, too, that our mass ratio is large enough to get us very close to the speed of light, carry us to a star one thousand light-years away, and slow us down again to normal speeds so we can visit one of the star's planets. The rocket is also to be capable of flying us back to earth—possibly by "refueling" during the stay at that distant solar system.

As we depart from the earth, the stars of the firmament will first appear in their familiar yellowish hue. As our vehicle builds up speed toward our target star, the Doppler effect will cause a striking change in this star's color. From its original yellow the light received from it will shift through green, blue, and violet, and toward ultraviolet—in other words, to higher frequencies. Simultaneously the color of the receding sun will slowly change from yellow to orange, red, and toward infrared—that is, to lower frequencies.

This is easy to understand: A boat running *against* the waves is hit by them at a *higher* frequency than a stationary pier is; a boat running *with* the waves, at a *reduced* frequency.

After about 3½ months our stellar photon rocket has reached about thirty percent of the speed of light. The frequency of the sun's peak radiation output now passes the border of the visible spectrum and moves into the infrared. As a result, the sun dims rapidly and soon becomes invisible. One month later the destination star likewise becomes invisible—the peak of its radiation intensity has shifted into the ultraviolet.

As our velocity keeps increasing, two circular dark spots are formed around the destination star and the sun, and keep growing in diameter. Between these blind "bow and stern spots," the stars of the firmament appear as a multicolored array of concentric circles, like a huge rainbow:

Near the black bow spot, the stars look violet. Further aft, they are blue and green. Abeam, they shine in their original yellowish hue. Still farther aft, they look orange; and the dark stern spot is surrounded by a ring of red stars.

Due to "relativistic" effects, the dark bow spot grows only to an opening angle of 43 degrees. After we exceed seventy-four percent of the speed of light (eleven months after departure), it begins to contract again. But the stern spot around the sun continues to grow steadily. Hence, as our traveling speed approaches the speed of light, the visible portion of the firmament will become compressed into an ever-narrowing rainbow around the invisible target star.

The opening angle of the yellow ring, in this rainbow, is a perfect yardstick for the ratio between our traveling speed and the speed of light. In analogy to the well-known Mach Number (ratio of flight speed to speed of sound), this ratio is sometimes called the Einstein Number.

In 6.6 years from the time of departure our speeding photon rocket hits Einstein Number .999998, and we are at the halfway point of our journey. However, on trying to measure the remaining distance to our destination star (now emitting predominantly X rays), we find it only about a light-year away! In fact, without further power application we would pass it a year later—7.6 years' "dilated ship's time" after departure—if we were to refrain from slowing down for our forthcoming visit.

But in order to visit one of the star's planets, we have to turn our ship around and use our photonic rocket thrust for braking. Of course, our slowing down means that we'll reach our target, not in another year, but much later. Only after another 6.6 years—13.2 years after departure—will we near our target at a relative approach speed close to zero. During the second 6.6 years—that is, during the retardation maneuver—all those celestial "rainbow" phenomena of the acceleration period will take place in reverse. Upon arrival, the firmament will look like its old self again.

If we had a telescope powerful enough to observe events on earth from our new vantage point, we would find our home planet very much as it was when we left it. But, being one thousand light-years away, we are actually watching events that happened on earth one thousand years ago. (This is the nondilated time that has elapsed *on earth* since we left.) The amazing thing is that, due to the time dilation aboard our speeding rocket, we have aged only 13.2 years during our outbound voyage.

Eerie as this may sound, it is all in perfect harmony with modern ideas of the laws of space and time. (Men today have the same difficulty in accepting the concept of relativistic time that our ancestors had in seeing how people "down under" in Australia could walk head down without dropping off the globe. But that is because our experience does not include very great distances and extremely high speeds.)

While the insights of modern physics permit us to dissect the anatomy of interstellar flight, we must forego rash conclusions that any such flights are imminent or feasible. We cannot yet even define an adequate power source. If we had it, many problems of using it would be beyond us. Other obstacles may be even more formidable. For instance, what would happen to an interstellar rocket that hit even a small meteoroid, if the collision were at nearly the speed of light?

In summary, with our present knowledge, we can respond to the challenge of stellar space flight solely with intellectual concepts and purely hypothetical analysis. Hardware solutions are still entirely beyond our reach and far, far away.

INDEX